GOSPEL CONVERSATIONS

Gospel Conversations

Desmond O'Donnell OMI

DOMINICAN PUBLICATIONS

First published (2015) by
Dominican Publications
42 Parnell Square
Dublin 1

ISBN 978-1-905604-28-9

British Library Cataloguing in Publications Data.
A catalogue record for this book is available
from the British Library.

Copyright © (2015) Desmond O'Donnell and Dominican Publications

Cover design by
David Cooke

Printed by
Sprint-Print
Dublin

Contents

Preface

As we read or pray the Gospels, we usually desire more information about the people and places, the context and customs described in its pages.

One purpose of this book is to offer some of the interesting facts discovered by scripture scholars, by historians and by archaeologists, about the culture, the habits and the lived experience of men and women mentioned in the Gospels.

The book also tries to enter into what may have been the thoughts and feelings of these people who appear in the pages of the Gospel. I do this by having them meet and talk with one another. Five of them open their hearts, as they seek help from a counsellor.

The world of the New Testament was unlike ours, because it was a different time and a different culture. The men and women who lived in Palestine 2,000 years ago were different from us also. These differences however, were only on the surface of their local experience and of their behaviour.

Human nature has always had the same basic needs – meaning in life, personal safety and security, self-transcendence and peace of heart, deep family love and togetherness, constant caring and touch, respect and acceptance from others, the enjoyment of celebration and freedom from guilt, some success and achievement and finally to share their thoughts and feelings with others. We all have these needs, and every person in the Gospel story had them too. The 20 conversations in this book try to show how this is so.

References to the Old Testament are more frequent in the first six chapters. These help to give the reader a look into the consciousness of people who appear in the Gospel stories.

The meaning of unfamiliar words and names, and books consulted, are given in the Glossary at the end of the book.

Each of these conversations could be enacted by two or three people, for presentation to an audience in a church, on a stage or in a school.

Hopefully, these conversations will help the reader to relate to, and to understand more easily, the people who played a central part in the life, death and resurrection of Jesus.

I am deeply grateful to Paddy Pender for her creative work throughout the text. I also wish to thank Ciaran O'Hare and Sister Kathleen O'Keefe for their careful proof-reading and their helpful suggestions.

Good News Imprisoned
John the Baptist meets Ezra, journalist

Ezra   Ezra is my name, John. I am the editor of the *Galilee Gazette*. We have been following your story since you burst onto the local scene from the bank of the Jordan. Now you are even bigger news since Herod has imprisoned you here in Machaerus. We cannot say it openly, but everyone knows that he has mixed feelings about you. He fears you but he admires you at the same time.

John   I do not remember seeing you before. Did you come to Aenon for baptism?

Ezra   No, not quite. My home is in Salim just beside Aenon, and, of course, our village was inundated with strangers while you were preaching and baptising nearby. Some of the local Pharisees kept trying to organize a protest against you but most of our villagers were on your side. Now I must explain that you *did* see me before. I came to you for an interview but as I approached, you almost pushed me into the Jordan. Then you asked me abruptly if I was repenting. I wasn't ready at that time...

John   So why are you here now, and how did you get into this fortress?

Ezra   Yes, it is a fortress all right but you see I overheard two of your disciples saying that they were allowed in to visit you, and that you sent them to ask Jesus who he was. Of course the editor of the *Gazette* has some influence too – shall we say – for getting into very private places!

John   But why are you here?

Ezra   Well, I have not come just as a reporter this time. I will tell you more about that if you can be patient; it is very personal. Your story became big news when it became clear that you were challenging the temple elite, and the entire ruling system. Now you are even bigger news since you are in prison, and you could be facing execution.

John   I ask you again, why have you come?

Ezra   Honestly, I am not yet clear and I do not have a reason that might satisfy you for why I have come. However, what I can say is that I am not against you. I suspect – no, I believe – that you have an important message for this country and for its people. Most of us know that the Temple is an institution supported by and driven by a system of power, status, and of course, money. Your friend Jesus is now on a collision course with the entire establishment, and I think they will imprison him too. He is describing you as a lamp, lit and shining. Most people remember that you talked about your unworthiness to untie his sandals, and that you said his arrival made your joy complete.

Quite apart from what he is saying, he is in trouble because of his connection with you. He too is challenging, not only the Priests, but the Scribes, the Pharisees, the Sadducees, the Tax Collectors and the violence of the Zealots.

John   Typical journalist! You missed the important things that I said about him. You people always go for what is a startling headline, and sometimes you miss the important point. You want a sensational story at all costs, sometimes at the cost of the real story.

Ezra   Tell me, then. What is the real story?

John   Our society and religion are led – or rather misled – by people who have a distorted image of God. They speak of a God of rigid law of which they claim to be the guardians. They also claim to be the only people who have direct access to God. Religion is a business for them, and a very profitable one too.

Ezra   But are they not the leaders appointed by God – apart from the Zealots fighting for political liberation, and perhaps the ascetical Essenes in their monasteries. Some say that Jesus was himself an Essene.

John   Some thought that he was an Essene, but he is

certainly not the monastic type. Nor is he notably ascetical. How could he be an Essene when he eats, drinks and socializes with the marginalized in public places? He preaches in the open, by the lakeside or on the hills, most of the time. Those Essenes are not in touch with real life. They think that they are the only people pleasing to God and that they have chosen a higher way of life than other people. Jesus is not supporting elitism of any kind. He reaches out in friendship to people who are on the edge of society.

Ezra Yes, one of my reporters got an excellent story about a prostitute who gate-crashed one of the parties. She washed Jesus' feet with tears of sorrow, and dried them with her hair. Jesus defended her against the Pharisee host, so no wonder they call him a drunkard and a friend of sinners.

John Yes, the Pharisees are a brood of vipers, misusing religion in their search for control, prestige and wealth. Our God is the very opposite. He is a God of service, a God of equality and a God of sharing. You understand that we have to oppose them and pay the price that I am paying now in this fortress. I lived with the Essenes for a few years but they are misguided too in their arrogant claims to be especially chosen by God. They are waiting for the wrong type of saviour. They are not compassionate to themselves or to others. That is why I left them, and I annoyed them by preaching in the Judean wilderness near their monastery. The locusts and wild honey are plentiful there.

Ezra I see, or rather I think I see. It was big news when your priestly father Zechariah was struck dumb and we told the story in the *Gazette*. We even published part of the song that he sang at your birth, about God's faithful love freeing his people from fear, forgiving their sins and foretelling your future work of guiding his people in the way of peace. You surely lack fear, John. Tell me more about your core demands.

John My central message is a demand for radical change, and as you know, the people flocked to hear that message. Of course those in power at any level did not like what I said. Even many of the good people walked away when I told them to share their tunics with the poor. The soldiers were angry when I told them not to intimidate or extort money from the people. The tax collectors were manifestly uncomfortable when I told them not to demand more than they ought. After hearing me, some in these groups acknowledged God's saving justice by accepting Baptism and change, but most of the Pharisees, the Sadducees and the lawyers continue to thwart God's plan for their lives.

Ezra   I think I now understand this idea of radical change, which you called conversion. You know that the Greeks among us are calling it *metanoia* – a word which describes what one wrestler did when he succeeded in getting hold of his adversary and hurled him off in the opposite direction. Is that the idea?

John   I chose a very old dynamic scriptural word – repentance – to describe one's willingness to allow God to turn one's life around, in the sense of a complete re-orientation. Sin is personal; it is not just breaking a law. I want people to turn away from sin, and then to turn towards God with all their being. God sent me to tell everyone, especially those leaders of religion and society, that they have turned away from him and gone in the wrong direction, on a path to self destruction. It has nothing to do with empty ritual or ascetical piety or obedience to a corrupt priesthood. They are leading others astray. It is like the blind leading the blind, as I heard Jesus told his disciples.

Ezra   That is pretty unwelcome news for religious leaders, and indeed for all of us, John.

John   Those leaders who claim to be educated should be familiar with the word *sub*, which is found over a thousand times in our scriptures. It indicates simply turning away from evil and back to God. I suppose that it why good people thought I was the Christ or Elijah or one of the prophets. I was just – in the words of Isaiah – a voice crying in the wilderness of Judea, asking everyone to prepare a way for the Lord and to make straight his paths. I did not want to be like a reed shaking in the wind or a grandee in fancy garments. I deliberately wore camel's hair, like Elijah did. I wanted my message – sorry, God's message – to be clear to all. Yes, I was only a voice.

Ezra No one can hear us speaking together now, so may I ask you about your confrontation with Herod?

John I suppose I could have kept quiet, but after all, he was a prominent leader. I did not think he would have been bothered by my remarks, until I openly challenged his lecherous behaviour. On the other hand, Herod, and, of course, his employers, the Romans, with whom he was colluding, were suspicious and uncomfortable about anyone who attracted large gatherings, even in the wilderness. Unrest and rebellion were, and still are, in the air.

I had to create a showdown with him when he took his brother Philip's wife. It was a topic of conversation everywhere. I had to condemn it, as I condemned the power, prestige and possession-seeking leaders, especially those on the Sanhedrin. As Jesus once described me, I was like God's winnowing-fan. A fan separates the good seed from the cockle. Yet, as you said, Herod was in awe of me, and he did come to hear me on one occasion.

Ezra It is reported that after your arrest, Jesus withdrew to Galilee. Perhaps he feels safer there, and maybe he has less courage than you.

John No, no. The Lamb of God will know when his time to be sacrificed has come.

Ezra You know John, that you really collided with the entire secular and religious establishment when you attracted people away from the temple. After all, it is the national shrine, and it figures centrally in Israel's self-understanding. It is God's house and his recognised dwelling place among his people. Is it not considered to be the only legitimate place of worship, as Deuteronomy says? Why did you not begin your mission there?

John   Of course, it is the sacred dwelling place of God's name, but the priests and other leaders have corrupted it. I did not want my message polluted and misunderstood or linked to the empty money-making rituals conducted there. The number of taxes collected in the temple precincts is great. I would not be surprised if Jesus does not eventually collide with the whole charade. God is not a God of distinctions. No, there is no place for me or my message in the temple as it is at this time. God can be worshipped anywhere, by people who first find him in their hearts and in their love for one another. We must move from temples to tables, from cult to community.

Ezra   How did you feel when some of your disciples decided to follow Jesus?

John   I was very happy indeed that I pointed him out to them. When they approached him, Jesus put the simple question to them, 'what do you want?' Then he invited them to come and see. In these words he reminded us that all religion is based on deep human desire. It is by invitation alone and never based on obligation. Any way of life, littered by obligations, destroys freedom and destroys human dignity.

     Andrew had been listening to me, and when I pointed Jesus out to him, he and a few of my other disciples went with him to where Jesus had begun to gather his own close followers. They stayed with him from four o'clock until the sun had set. Then Andrew brought his brother Peter to Jesus. Yes, my mission had ended and my joy was complete. It was time for him to increase and for me to decrease – and to eventually disappear.

Ezra   I think I would like to be baptised by you, John.

John   Thinking about it is not enough. Although my baptism is only with water, it symbolises radical commitment. You must move from thought to decision. If I were to baptise you, how would your life change? Perhaps a weekly visit to the synagogue and doing religious things during the week? Would you still be just a journalist looking for any story, or would justice and truth be your priority? When you have reflected more about your whole mindset, Ezra, come to see me again.

Shalom!

Good News Beheaded

John the Baptist and Ezra continue their conversation

Ezra I am sorry to have come back so soon, John, but one of the guards was heard saying that Herod is going to execute you. Did you know that Herodias has requested that your head be given to her on a platter? One of the waiters at Herod's banquet heard Herodias' daughter use the word 'immediately'. So, that is why I am here. I really want to repent and to be baptised by you.

John Have you heard the Messiah yet?

Ezra No. I had intended going to meet him, but after your arrest he went off to Galilee, so I missed him. Did you ever meet with him yourself?

John He blessed me in my mother's womb when his mother, Mary, came to visit us, all the way from Nazareth to Ain Karem in the hills where we lived. Of course, I did not know this, but my mother, Elizabeth, told me that I leapt with joy in her womb when Mary arrived so soon after the angel had visited her. My mother said that she immediately felt filled with the Holy Spirit. Then Jesus and I met and played together as children a few times, despite the distance between our homes. That was before either of us received his mission.

Ezra Mission? What does that mean?

John Well, my mother told me that after she praised Mary for her faith, Mary felt inspired to sing a prophetic song, praising God and describing Jesus' mission. Mother never forgot it because it was filled with scriptural quotations well known to every Jewish believer. It was easy to remember, and she often repeated it to me. You will become familiar with its description of the Messiah's mission when you speak to Mary. You understand, Ezra, that after receiving my water-baptism you will have to be baptised in the Holy Spirit by one of Jesus' disciples?

Ezra I am very willing and even anxious to hear anything you want to tell me about this man Jesus before I meet him.

John You already know that God is the mighty Saviour of Israel, and that it is our privilege to listen with humility to his life-giving word. Then he will do great things in us and for us. His name is holy, and that word means totally beyond any imperfection, totally different. Our central story is God's fidelity to his promises in the Covenant. We can only stand in reverent awe before him. It is Jesus' mission to remind Israel of all this.

Ezra Even though my life has not been a holy one and maybe not even a religious one, all that you are saying is surely in my bones, as a Jew. We Israelites breathe it, almost from birth.

John But Ezra, it has to be consciously in your heart, actively in your hands and in your feet. Do you have a phylactery on your forehead when you pray?

Ezra My parents rarely missed a Sabbath at the synagogue, and they always made me wear one when we prayed. But then I left home, and you understand that a newspaper office can be a very secular place. So, over time I stopped wearing it.

John Jesus' mission was described more deeply in Mary's prophetic words when they foretold his preference for the poor and the powerless. He condemned the avaricious and those who sought power. Primarily, his mission was to recall all of us to the faith of our father, Abraham. Can you hear this message deep in your heart, Ezra?

Ezra Yes, yes I can, and I accept it fully.

John But Ezra, there is more. Jesus is no mere prophet; he is the promised Messiah, the Christ sent by The Holy One. The messianic signs are present in his life – now the blind can see, the paralysed can walk, the lepers' skin is cleansed and the deaf can hear. He is preaching the good news of God's love to everyone, especially to the poor and to those on the margins of society and on the margins of religious groups.

Ezra   I did hear that Jesus was doing these things, but I am the doubting type. It is good to receive reassurance from you, John.

John   And there is still more – much, much more.

Ezra   And you baptised Jesus; I don't understand …

John   Neither do I fully understand. At first I refused to baptise him, but he insisted upon it, saying, 'Leave it like this for the time being'. Then he continued, 'It is proper that we should in this way do all that uprightness demands'. Only then did I baptise him.

Ezra   Almost everyone believes that Jesus is a prophet because he disturbs the evil status quo, just like Hosea, Isaiah and Jeremiah did. But there have been so many men claiming to be Messiahs or saviour figures, that it is difficult to tell who is authentic. Mind you, I am a modern person and I deal with what is visible, not with what may or may not have been promised in ancient history. I interviewed one of the Qumran monks and he said that they still await their anointed priest. He had not heard of this man called Jesus.

The Sadducees say that Jesus does not know the Law nor the traditions passed on by word of mouth. They do not believe in a future life about which Jesus constantly speaks. Like yourself he preaches mostly far away from the temple.

In fact, he has even foretold the destruction of the temple, and he claims that he is God's new temple. However, he certainly does not look like the mighty and majestic Messiah that most people expect. One Zealot, called Simon, has been seen among his disciples, but Jesus does not appear to be confronting the occupying Romans with violence, as the Zealots do. And of course, everyone knows that Jesus was born in an obscure village called Bethlehem, and that until now he earned his living as a carpenter.

John   Enough, Ezra! Your knowledge of the Holy Scriptures is as limited as your religious practice.

Ezra   Will you help me, John? I can judge only by what I see.

John   Well, our hopes for the Messiah have been over idealized. We are all inclined to imagine and to create in our minds what we are expecting or hoping for. Just like our idea of salvation, our idea of a Messiah could easily develop secular, nationalistic and materialistic overtones. Some sort of superhuman figure has often been expected. The Holy One sent saviours before now to deliver his people – men like Moses, David, Nehemiah and Ezra, the man after whom you were named. In recent centuries the idea of a king-saviour, a political saviour with the power of The Holy One, has been strong.

Ezra   No wonder I was confused, but I believe you now, John, that Jesus is the Messiah.

John   He is more than the Messiah, Ezra. This carpenter from Nazareth is the Son of God, but not only as every Jew is God's son or daughter. He is different. I saw the Spirit descend to rest on him, in the form of a dove. Suddenly there was a voice from heaven saying, 'This is my Son, the beloved, with whom I am well pleased. Listen to him'. Yes, The Holy One had come to visit his people, and he was led immediately by the Spirit, out into the desert. Then the words of Isaiah came to my mind and my lips:

> Land of Zebulun! Land of Naphtali!
> Way of the sea beyond the Jordan.
> Galilee of the nations!
> The people that lived in darkness
> have seen a great light;
> on those who sat in the region and shadow of
>   death
> a light has dawned.

My mission was clear. I was destined to be a prophet of the Most High and to prepare a way before him. Israel's bridegroom has come. The Holy One has sent

him and he has spoken The Holy One's own words.
I am blessed to be the bridegroom's friend. God his
Father loves him, and he has given him the Spirit
without reserve. He has entrusted everything into his
hands. Anyone who believes in him has eternal life.

Ezra John, I believe. I thoroughly regret that I have
written some negative editorial comment about
you in the *Gazette*. Yes, John, I am sorry, very sorry
indeed. I came here, partially in fear of you and with
very mixed motives, but I have grown to admire
you, to believe in what you say and to love you as a
friend.

John You too are a son of God, Ezra, a righteous man, and
… yes … a friend.

Ezra I repent and I believe. Now I want to begin my
journey with your baptism of water.

John There is a pool at the back of the fortress, and we can
use that. Come with me, my friend …

The noise of chains and marching soldiers approaching can be heard

Sorry Ezra, it is too late. They have come for my
head. Good bye, my friend. Please remember to greet
Jesus for me when you meet him, and remember me
to his mother also.

A Visit

Mary and Elizabeth share their joy

Elizabeth   Mary, I almost fell as I hurried down the valley to meet you. I am so glad that you decided to make this long journey to Ain Karem. Shalom, Mary. Welcome.

Mary   Yes, Elizabeth, it was a long journey but I am already refreshed from your warm embrace. Shalom.

Elizabeth   You are blessed among women, and the babe in your womb is also blessed! Why am I so favoured that the mother of my Lord has come to visit me? The moment the sound of your greeting reached my ears, the babe in my womb leapt for joy. Blessed woman, who believed that every word spoken by God to you, would come true.

Mary   Yes, I am overflowing with the presence of The Holy One. Inside me I am dancing the song of my Saviour. The Holy One accepted my lowliness, and look what happened – I am the most fortunate woman on earth. What God has done for me will never be forgotten. His name is holy; he is apart from all others. His mercy flows, wave after wave, on those who are in awe before him. He bared his arm and showed his strength. He scattered the bluffing braggarts. He knocked tyrants off their thrones and pulled victims out of the mud. The starving poor feasted at a banquet, the callous rich were left out in the cold. He embraced his chosen child, Israel, remembering him and heaping his mercies upon him, piling them high. It is exactly as he promised, beginning with Abraham, and right up to the present.

Elizabeth   Now you must refresh yourself further and have a bath, Mary. Take some of this olive oil to use afterwards – 'Oil to make your face to shine', the Psalm says. We had a great growth in our olive grove this year. Later, you can wear my veil and my best garment with its embroidered girdle.

Later that same day

Elizabeth Mary, you look beautiful. I'm sure you enjoyed your bath. Thank you for the basket of perfumes and henna that you brought me from Ashkelon. Come now, I have prepared some food and a glass of wine for us. Do you like honey in yours? The men usually sweeten the wine with honey for us, and most women like it that way. I prefer it without honey, even though Zechariah often quotes Sirach, warning us that wine encourages levity and it can lead intelligent men astray.

Zechariah is having his siesta now. His inability to speak since his last service in the Temple has stressed him very much. The whole village is talking about him being struck dumb by the angel and so is everyone in the villages around us. And of course, he misses his meetings with the local men in the village square. The doctors cannot explain what happened. I wonder if his speech will ever return.

Mary I pray that it will, Elizabeth. I suppose the women have much to talk about too when they heard the good news of your unexpected pregnancy. How are you feeling now?

Elizabeth My everyday tasks, as you know them – baking bread, washing clothes, cooking food, cleaning, and working on the spinning wheel – I can manage. However, I find grinding the seed for flour very difficult, partially due to my age, of course. I often wonder about Proverb's description of the ideal wife having to work so hard – spinning and making linen garments and girdles for sale. Thankfully, Zechariah has asked his niece to help me.

Mary Yes, Joseph said that I too will soon need some assistance with my household tasks. At least we do not have to work at inns or in shops as some women and most widows are forced to do. I heard that some husbands insist that their wives take an oath to promise that they will never keep any of their earned money for themselves. A few of the widows in Nazareth had to learn endless lamentations in order to wail at funerals, and worst of all, in their poverty, some were forced into prostitution. Many widows suffer much.

Elizabeth Yes, a few widows here had to practise divination, magic and the explanation of dreams in order to become witches – all of which is strongly condemned in the *Torah*. It is all very sad.

Three months later

Zechariah What joy! At last I have my speech back and we have been blessed with the arrival of our baby son.

Mary Yes, it is great news for you, Zechariah. Our experiences have been somewhat similar in meeting God's messengers.

Zechariah Indeed they have, Mary. I just overheard you tell Elizabeth about your dialogue with the angel. Gabriel assured me that my son would be great. I know that he told you the same about your son, but, remember, he added that your child would be Son of the Most High. He said that my son will prepare a people, but Mary, your son is destined to rule the people.

Mary The angel also said that both of our sons will be prophets.

Zechariah Yes, but he promised that your son would be more than a prophet. He will be the Son of The Most High. My son John was promised to be filled with the Holy Spirit but I heard you say that the *overshadowing* of the Spirit will make Jesus The Holy One. Yes, Elizabeth and I are indeed very privileged people, but the similarities between our sons are very, very limited. Now, please tell me about your 105 league journey to Ain Karem.

Mary Well, first of all I travelled to Jerusalem with a small group of pilgrims on their way there, and I rested with some cousins for a few days. Those strategic military roads built by the Romans are a blessing for all travellers, especially for those in the group caravans or in the chariots of the wealthy. The new roads also make it much easier for those who walked part of the journey. Of course we rested in the heat of the day, but we walked seven kilometres before sunrise, and seven after sunset each evening.

We took the shorter route through Samaria – with all its risks. Our stronger men carried staves and clubs to protect us. After leaving Galilee, so green and fertile, I was a little homesick, especially as we faced into the rugged hills. Then the sight and smell of the orchards and vineyards planted everywhere, even between the rocks around your villages, lifted my spirit.

Elizabeth   Now, tell me again about the angel Gabriel's visit.

Mary   Well, in contrast to Zechariah I held no official position among the people, and because I am a woman I would not be described as righteous in obeying the *Torah*. The encounter with Gabriel did not even take place in a worship setting as Zechariah's did in the Temple. I was young, female and poor. As you know, we women are not bound to go to Jerusalem annually and, unlike men, we are not bound to recite the *Shema* twice daily.

Elizabeth   Perhaps that is why Gabriel said, 'Hail, gifted lady. You have found favour with God'. It was all gift, all grace. But were you not fearful, Mary?

Mary   Yes, I was fearful in the presence of an angel, and I was confused so awesome was the message. Even though we women do not study the scriptures, and have little religious instruction, we are filled with Messianic hopes, like everyone else. Our nation has endured great humiliation, first by the Seleucids of Antioch and now we suffer under the Romans. We really need a saviour to set us free.

Elizabeth   Of course you were looking forward to your marriage to Joseph by then.

Mary   Indeed I was. During our 12 months of betrothal I was collecting my dowry and Joseph was building our new home. I was almost paralysed with fear when Joseph, in his goodness, told my family that he would have to hide me away, quietly.

Elizabeth Until then, I suppose you would have had to face the thought of divorce in the provincial Sanhedrin court with its 23 judges.

Mary And there was of course the terrible thought that Joseph and the neighbours could consider that I had been unfaithful. I would then have been ostracised and been the butt of constant humiliation.

Elizabeth The Lord has preserved you because, unlike Zechariah, you did not question his word. You asked only how it was going to happen, in keeping with your virgin state.

Mary Yes, I know it was the Spirit who guided and enabled me to respond, 'Let what you have said be done to me'. Now I experience great peace. During the few brief meetings before our wedding, Joseph told me about the Messianic promises, especially in the Psalms. He told me that the prophet Daniel spoke about his visions of the Son of Man. He also told me that Isaiah foretold how God would eventually redeem the faithful remnant of his people. He quoted Micah too but I have forgotten the reassuring words. My father Joachim joined Joseph and elaborated on what Joseph had told me.

Elizabeth So now you return to Nazareth and to your family. You have brought me much joy in your spontaneous visit and in your act of service to me while I am with child in my old age. Remember Gabriel's words to you, 'Do not be afraid, Mary'. Zechariah and I will pray for your safe arrival home.

Mary Shalom, my friends, and thank you for your love and support.

A Wedding Celebration

Joseph and Mary celebrate their wedding

Joseph   Well, alone at last, together with my beautiful wife.

Mary   At last! And it is great. Even though families and friends like ours are gifts from God, it is good to be alone.

Joseph   It was seven wonderful days of celebration. You must be exhausted, Mary.

Mary   Yes, I surely feel tired but I am the happiest woman in Israel. And our guests made a wonderful contribution to the wedding and festivities.

Joseph   Mary, I am delighted to see your lovely long black hair uncovered for me alone. When I remember that poor Rachel had to sell her beautiful hair so that Akiba, the greatest rabbi of his time, could study the *Torah*, it makes me feel sad.

Mary   Your uncle Thaddeus told me how a rabbi once said that God spent most of his time arranging marriages. I wonder how long it took him to arrange ours. Even the first part of our betrothal – the *shiddukin* – seemed lengthy to me, when our parents were discussing our suitability for each other. I remember well, it was just after my twelfth birthday. You were nearly 20 then, and a successful carpenter-blacksmith.

Joseph   I found the *kiddushin*, the second part of our espousal, after we had accepted our parents' recommendation that we should marry, much more testing for my patience. From the first time I saw you, Mary, even under the head veil, I knew that I wanted to marry you. I prayed constantly that God would grant my wish.

I was nervous too until my father's friend came back with the news that your father Joachim was willing to talk to my father. Of course, in a village of 40 or so families and with my Davidic ancestry, combined with your priestly heritage coming through Zechariah, Elizabeth's husband, it was likely that we would be matched. We can both laugh now at the common phrase, 'Can anything good come out of Nazareth?'

Mary   I have never been out of Nazareth, not even to the city of Sepphoris where you worked to help erect Herod's fine buildings. Amazing, really, with the city only two hours from Nazareth by foot. Some day you must bring me there, Joseph.

Joseph   The Scribe who accompanied me to meet your father, in order to sign the *ketuvah* marriage contract, lives in Sepphoris and he would welcome us to his home for a visit any time. Yes, Mary, I will certainly bring you there.

Mary   I remember smiling when he told me that I would receive at least 200 *zuzim* and my dowry of 50 *zuzim* would be returned, if you divorced me. That thought was far from my mind when you arrived on the evening of our wedding. You were dressed so elegantly, Joseph.

Joseph   You were so beautifully dressed too, Mary, and Jeremiah's words came to mind, 'Can a maiden forget her ornaments or a bride her attire?' Certainly I will never forget how you looked.

Mary   I remember it so well. On that Wednesday morning – it's lovely to share that customary day with all other couples getting married – I was anointed and given the crown of flowers to wear over my long tresses which flowed loosely under my veil. Then my father gave me the traditional blessing, 'May you never return home as a widow or divorcee, may you be the mother of a thousand children and may your descendants possess the gates of those who hate them'.

Joseph   How happy and proud I was to see you carried high on the magnificently adorned family chair that my mother had used on her wedding day. I was bursting with pride as your wedding procession moved through the narrow lanes of the village, towards my home. The music of the lute, the pipes and the drums was powerful, and everyone in the village rejoiced with us. I love the custom that even the study of the *Torah* can be interrupted to join a marriage procession. And I amazed that the *Talmud* dictates that even a funeral must go into a side street to allow the wedding party to pass. Nazareth was all ours on that Wednesday.

Mary   So many people greeted me and waved myrtle and palm branches on each side of my chair. The children enjoyed catching and picking up the nuts and roasted corn ears that were thrown to them.

Joseph   You remember that, as the procession approached my home, I had to hurry ahead to greet you there, where I was to hear the rabbi say, 'Take her according to the Law of Moses and of Israel', to which I had to reply, 'Be thou my wife in marriage according to the Law of Moses and of Israel'. I did it so willingly and with all my heart.

Mary   Then our friends and guests said a beautiful prayer which I cannot remember now.

Joseph   They said, 'May the Lord be with this young woman who is coming into the house, so that she can build it up with children, as Rachel and Leah built up the house of Israel. May she prosper and be renowned'.

Mary   Only you and I know how meaningless was the gesture of holding aloft the hen and the cock as symbols of fertility, praying that our union would be fruitful.

Joseph   Then I led you proudly into my home, followed by the few who could fit into the house. The others were happy to remain outside. That space was divided with the reed screen to separate the men from the women. And we observed the custom that the men washed from the large stone jars first. I too washed before joining you under the canopy.

Mary   It was beautiful, Joseph, as we sat under the canopy and were blessed as a couple, 'May the Lord our God, King of the Universe, who has created everything and made us in his own image, bless this young couple, as He blessed Adam and Eve in the garden of Eden'. Elizabeth taught me that prayer a long time before my wedding. It was recited over the first cup of wine, was it not? I was so pleased that your family and friends arranged to have enough wine to last the seven days – 'wine to make your heart rejoice', as we pray so often in the Psalm.

Joseph We Jews enjoy all the gifts of God. Sirach told us, 'Do not deprive yourself of a day's enjoyment'. I often wonder how the monks in Qumran near the Dead Sea persevere in their frugal, ascetical life.

Bringing the salt as the first thing to our marriage table helped to remind us of the salt used on the Temple altar. Let me now recite our never forgotten prayer of grace before meals – 'Blessed are you, Lord God of all creation. Through your goodness we have this bread and wine to offer for your blessing. May this fruit of the earth and work of human hands become for us the food and drink of life', and your response, 'Blessed be God forever'. Sirach was so right when he wrote that wine and music bring gladness to the heart.

Mary Although I was tired, Joseph, I enjoyed our meal as I used the folded bread to scoop up the tasty mutton stew which we can so rarely afford. It was perfect with the lentils, beans and pickled onions. I noticed that after the first day most people were served fish in brine, from the lake of Genesareth, and they were happy with that. I was very glad to be free from the canopy after the first day, and to withdraw quietly from the crowd when I felt like it. I was already experiencing the holy babe within me, and I needed time alone to reflect and pray.

Joseph The dancing of the young men was skilful, especially when some of them juggled pomegranates at the same time. When they came to give me their personal greetings, each of them commented how blessed I was to have you as my wife. It gave me the opportunity to thank them individually for their part in planning our beautiful wedding day.

Mary   All of the older men came to amuse me with stories
and give me riddles. They told me that custom
dated back to Samson, who, in this manner, had
entertained the guests at his own wedding. I enjoyed
old Rufus best, even though I could not understand
everything he said.

We could go on talking forever about the great
day, but it is getting very late, and you are very tired.

Joseph   Just one more thing, Mary. One of my friends who
works in Sepphoris told me that, yesterday evening,
when all the people had returned from the fields and
gardens, the town-crier climbed up to the roofs of the
highest houses in the city. He announced that Caesar
Augustus had ordered all the men in his empire to
be counted, the Jews according to their tribal descent
in their own city, and the Gentiles according to their
place of permanent abode. Of course we know that
all this is intended to assure an oath of allegiance to
him from everyone, without exception. He is very
insecure, and, of course, the Zealots are making him
more so. Recently they killed three more Roman
soldiers.

Mary   Does this mean that we must travel soon to your
family city of Bethlehem?

Joseph   Yes, Mary, my donkey is healthy but I must get
stronger sandals for the journey. Closer to our
departure we must put together barley loaves, dried
cheese, figs, dates and perhaps some olives if they are
in season. I should bring some of my tools of trade
too, lest I need to look for work along the journey.
And, of course, we will need the leather bucket with
its rope, to draw water from the wells along the way.

Mary   It will be wonderful for me to see Samaria, Mount
Tabor, the township of Endor, the ruins of Ahab's
summer palace, and all the places where our
ancestors fought many battles. I always heard that
going through the Samaritan country could be
unsafe. So I wonder should we take the longer way
through the Jordan valley?

Joseph   Yes, we will avoid the Samaritan country. It is safer to do so. Of course, we will be accompanied by other small caravans, and we will also meet many people on their return journey.

May it be thy will, O Lord our God, to conduct us in peace.

Mary   Amen, Joseph.

Back from Bethlehem

Joseph, Mary, Joachim and Anna share the joy of Jesus' birth

Joachim   Your mother and I are so glad to welcome Joseph and yourself back home to Nazareth. Such a long journey and such a wonderful event. We had hoped that you would be back for the birth, but God disposes. We were sad that our age prevented us from going with you.

Anna   Oh, what a beautiful baby!

Mary   Jesus is his name, just as the angel commanded me to call him.

Joachim   Now we must hear about your first long journey away from Nazareth, through Jerusalem, to Bethlehem.

Joseph   Of course, I told Mary that women do not have to go for registration. The proclamation says 'every male…' But how could I leave her at home? I'd be worrying all the way there and back!

Joachim   Well, we gave you a great send off as we gave the customary blessing, 'Depart in peace'. I notice that the new sandals I gave you seem well worn now. Your mother's heavy cloak of coarse wool must have been very useful during the cold nights.

Joseph   You remember that as the Law binds us, I managed, with your help, to pay all our debts and I returned all the pledges and objects loaned to us before everyone kissed us goodbye.

Mary   On the winding path, as we waved good bye for the last time into the distance, Joseph and I said the customary journey prayer many times: 'May it be thy will, O Lord, our God, to conduct us in peace, direct our steps, and to deliver us from the enemy or attacks along the way.'

Joseph   It was a change for my donkey, who was used to carrying timber and tools to Sepphoris, to have Mary sitting on its back from time to time. Of course, the two wicker baskets on each side of the donkey had our provisions, and they were heavy too.

Mary Thanks for the advice about which route to take. Given my condition, it certainly was safer taking the longer route this time, to avoid travelling through Samaria. We took the Jordan valley path instead and then through Naim. There we joined the great caravan route, a branch of the Via Maris which runs from the sea to Beth-Shan.

Joseph It was Mary's first sight of Mount Tabor with its dense oak forests. She said that its shape reminded her of a potter's wheel.

Mary Every part of our journey was full of memories of great historical events, and of battles with glorious victories and tragic defeats in the history of our people. My faith assured me that all these events were part of the mysterious plans of the Lord our God. Every one of them shaped the destiny of Israel.

Mary When Joseph pointed out the town of Shunnen in the distance, I immediately thought of the wealthy woman who gave food to Elisha. Even then women were part of God's plan too.

Joachim How did you know this piece of history, Mary?

Mary My cousin Elizabeth told me how God quietly needed and involved women all through his divine plan for our salvation.

Joseph When we were able to look over the valley of Esdraelon, sweeping down to the Mediterranean, Mary was breathless at the magnificent sight before us and we stopped to enjoy it.

Joseph Beth-Shan is still an opulent city, inhabited mostly by Gentiles, with their temple, theatre and their amphitheatre outside the walls. We said the customary prayer on leaving, 'Blessed is he who can root out idolatry from our land'. And we repeated it often as we crossed the stony plain of Rephaim where David overcame the Philistines.

Mary   As we passed Beth-Shan, Joseph told me that it is
the only city where the lepers are allowed to roam
around freely. However, they had to shout, 'Unclean,
unclean', wear torn clothes, and keep their hair
hanging over their faces. It was a terrible sight, and
I prayed for Naaman's cure to be given to the many
poor lepers we saw.

Now I must tell you about something beautiful
that happened. We paused at the tomb of Rachel,
whom Jacob loved at first sight. You remember that
he served her father for 14 years in lieu of a dowry.
Joseph and I renewed our love for each other on that
holy spot. Yes, it was a beautiful experience.

Joachim   By now you were near Jericho with its great fertile
land, thanks to Elisha's miracle when he put salt into
the well.

Mary   The gardens of Jericho are breathtaking. I recalled
how our ancestors marched around the city seven
times before the walls fell. Joseph told me the terrible
story of how our army shamefully destroyed every
man, woman and child in the city.

Joseph   From there we began the climb to Jerusalem, which
was about 20 kilometres away. We had to pause
often, and each time we did, we looked back. Our
hearts were lifted and our faith was strengthened as
we saw Mount Nebo where Moses died, after God
allowed him to glimpse the Promised Land. Our poor
donkey found the climb difficult.

Just six kilometres past Jerusalem, my family city
Bethlehem – the House of Bread – was soon in sight.
How proud I felt to think that it was mentioned even
in the Amara letters, 14 centuries ago. Ruth and Boaz
married here, and Ruth became the grandmother of
David's father Jesse. Later, David made Bethlehem
his royal city before he moved to Jerusalem. Yes, the
House of David is a great family.

Mary   Of course, the city was thronged with people who
had come to register. There was no room in the inns
but the *mitzvah* obligation – to take the stranger
in – was strong there. A poor woman who noticed

my condition took us to her home, despite the fact that only a stable was available. Immediately after the birth, she brought warm water to wash the baby and the salt to harden his skin. Having wrapped him in the strips of cloth that we had brought with us, she laid him in the animals' feeding trough that Joseph had arranged so carefully. He encouraged me greatly during the birth with a saying from the Book of Exodus, 'Hebrew women are not like the Egyptian women. They are vigorous and give birth before a midwife comes to them'

Joseph   Our first visitors were from the lowest stratum of society – shepherds. It was amazing to have these very poor men coming to us, when you think of our prejudices against them – treating them like robbers, usurers and pigeon-racers, and forbidding everyone to buy anything from them because we presume that everything they have is stolen. They brought us some milk and they believed the story that good news awaited them when they found a baby lying in a manger. It will be great to tell Jesus about these good shepherds when he grows up. Our culture never applies the word 'good' to shepherds.

Joachim   Did you have the baby circumcised, between the eighth day and the twelfth?

Mary   Yes, Joseph had the *mohel* perform the delicate operation. I watched him anxiously as he sucked the blood and applied the plaster of crushed cumin seeds. We named the baby Jesus, which as you know means 'Yahweh is salvation' – Jesus Bar-Joseph. Joseph paid the five Tyrian shekels of redemption money to a priest.

Joachim   Of course, you presented Jesus in the Temple on your way back.

Joseph   Yes, but first I had to buy the token marked 'doves'. Then Mary, with the baby in her arms joined the other women waiting at the magnificent Nicanor gate. They were led by the priest who collected the tokens, before he picked out two doves for each token. He wrung the necks of the birds, and sprinkled their blood above and below the red line on the altar. Then incense was burned and he recited a blessing over the prostrate women.

Mary On the way out we met a righteous and devout man called Simeon who asked to take the baby in his arms. He blessed God for allowing him to live to see Jesus, whom he described as a light for the Gentiles and a glory for his people Israel. He said that my baby was destined for the fall and rise of many in Israel, and to be a sign that will be disputed.

The lovely old prophetess Anna also met us. She spoke continuously about the baby to everyone who awaited liberation for Jerusalem.

Joseph Mary, you did not tell your father about the other part of Simeon's prophesy.

Mary Then he said … *(pause)*

Joachim Please tell me. Mary.

Mary Simeon looked lovingly but sadly at me …
and …
and he said …
that a sword would cut through my very life.

A Passover Journey

Father and daughter discuss Passover

Mary   It has been a marvellous experience, Abba. Passover is surely a great celebration of our liberating God.

Joachim   Indeed, Mary! It is great to have you back in the village and in your own home. I was so sorry that I could not travel to the feast this time, the first one I missed since I was 12 years of age. Sadly, the three-day journey would have been too much for your mother and myself. Of course, I still paid the temple tax, 30 days before the feast. It annoys me how the Adar money-changers arrive in Nazareth every year to change our bronze coins into the silver Tyrian shekel and charge 2% for the transaction. The priests themselves are exempt from the temple tax; and, for a very different reason, so are the women, slaves and minors. Imagine, women are in the same category as the slaves and minors. Although I am an old man, that still makes me angry.

Mary   It is strange to hear that Deuteronomy commands, 'three times a year all your males shall appear before the Lord'. Men are obliged to go up to Jerusalem for the Passover, but women, slaves and minors are not.

Joachim   Of course, customs change, and males no longer go up to the city three times a year. Usually once a year, at Passover time, is sufficient. People tend to ignore excessive legalism and change comes about slowly.

Mary   I am so glad that you prevailed upon Joseph to take me there for the first time. Now I am eager to share in this central feast of our faith every year.

Joachim   How did Jesus enjoy it? Although it is not written in the law, our wisdom says, 'one or two years before the boys come of age, at thirteen, they should be exercised in religious obligations, so that they become versed in God's commandments'.

Mary   He says that he is going to come and visit you

himself, because he would like to share his experience with you, and ask you some questions. He has already developed the habit of asking all sorts of questions about the Law.

Joachim   That is praiseworthy.

Mary   Yes indeed, but his curiosity and questioning have caused Joseph and me great anxiety.

Joachim   What do you mean?

Mary   Well, on our journey home, at Lebonah, our first stop, we felt safe and happy that Jesus was with some of his friends in the party. He mixes well with his own age-group and with adults too.

I became a little anxious one evening, so Joseph and I went from caravan to caravan looking for him and asking if anyone had seen him. To our alarm, he was nowhere to be found. Our caravan had to return to the city to find him. We pushed our way through the crowds and after two nights with little or no sleep, we found him at last – in the Temple, sitting among the teachers and asking them questions.

Joachim   And what did you say to him?

Mary   I said, 'My child, why have you done this to us? See how worried your father and I have been, looking everywhere for you'. He gave us a rather strange, vague answer about how he had to be involved in his father's business. I was very confused, and I still do not understand the meaning of what he said.

All I can do is to keep the whole affair in my heart until The Holy One gives me more insight. It is all part of the mystery of this child. For now, it is great that we are all safely home again.

Joachim   Indeed, but I suppose you are both tired. I am sure the entire journey must have been another enlightening history lesson for you, even after your previous journey to Bethlehem. And, of course, it was all new for Jesus.

Mary   He kept asking questions as usual. When we were passing through Samaria he wanted to know why the

Samaritans were preparing to go to Mount Gerizim and not to Jerusalem. On the second day we passed through the undulating plateau of Dothan, where the brothers of Joseph had watched over their father's flock. Even though we had told him about it many times before, Jesus wanted to hear the story of Joseph appearing in his flamboyant robes once again.

Joachim   In my old memory I can still hear the ram's horn, the *shofar*, sounding, to have the Temple doors opened. The people crowded into the vast courts to take part in the morning *tamid* service, the solemn sacrifice of one lamb, for the whole Jewish nation. How did you manage with the dense crowds on the narrow streets?

Mary   It was difficult, especially when the loaded donkeys had to pass through. But Herod's new eight-feet-wide, white stone-paved straight streets made travel much easier. The soft babel of low Greek sounded so different from our provincial Aramaic. The more prominent Pharisees stood out because of their oversized phylacteries and *zizits* hanging from the ends of their cloaks. As they stood out prominently to pray three times each day, Jesus looked them up and down; and, of course, he asked more questions.

Joachim   I presume that Herod's palace is still an imposing building? His son Archelaus occupies it now. Doesn't the Temple give great employment to the traders and artisans and a thriving business to the sellers in the bazaars? Did you notice the contrast between the building of the lower clergy and Mount Zion where the high priestly oligarchy and the Sadducean aristocracy have their grand houses? In my old age I can see clearly the prominence of corrupt hierarchy all over our land.

Mary   At the Temple we passed through the Court of the Gentiles and ascended the 14 steps to the Court of the Women. Jesus – he was asking questions again – wanted to know why the women could not go any further. It seemed to annoy him when we waved to each other because I had to stay behind. Yet, we women could see the huge curtain that hid the sanctuary. All the white-clad, turbaned priests were quite a sight for the young boy from Nazareth to see. They were such a contrast to the beggars at the Temple gate to whom a gift from passers-by earned remission of sins for the giver. Jesus wondered about this too.

Joachim   It is interesting how the oral tradition insists that when you were purified you had to leave the Temple Mount on the left, lest you touch the unpurified people entering on the right. When purified you had to process around the sanctuary, prostrating yourself 13 times as you went.

And did you notice the Scribes at their tables, quills behind their ears, ready to write contracts? The market inspectors were there too checking the weights, and measuring the cups to ensure the just *ephah* and *hin* as commanded by the Law. Did you know that the population of Jerusalem doubled at the time of the festivals?

Mary   Jesus was fascinated by the variety of rituals, and he asked what all of it had to do with The Holy One. He went forward with Joseph and our male friends, carrying the paschal lamb without blemish under his arm. I noticed that he kept looking down at its face. I heard that the oral tradition forbids us to use a lamb with one ear larger than the other, or even one with a bone missing in its tail. No defect is permitted. Of course, the bleating of so many thousands of lambs was a new sound for us.

Jesus talked a lot about seeing the men slaughter the lambs, and the priest catching the blood in bowls to throw it against the base of the altar. He said that there was blood everywhere as the barefooted blood-sprinkled priests removed the sacrificial parts which they put on silver trays before flinging them into the fire on the altar. Then the carcasses were given to the pilgrims while the Levites led the men singing the *Hallel* psalms.

Joachim   I was sad not to have been with you for that Passover meal which expresses the very core of our faith – God's saving act for his people. It is so solemn when we follow the ritual of washing our hands, and have our four cups of red wine mixed with spice and warm water. I always joined with great fervour in the prayers that were recited between the filling of the cups.

Mary   After the second cup of wine, it was beautiful to hear Jesus ask Joseph, 'Why is this night different from other nights, when all bread is unleavened and meat has to be roasted on a spit made of pomegranate wood, not stewed or cooked?' And then we heard Joseph remind everyone: 'A wandering Aramean was my father...' until he finished the entire section. Then we ate it without breaking a bone, as the Law requires. After filling the cups for the third time we sang the second part of the *Hallel,* and then we enjoyed the fourth cup. A few of the older people fell asleep.

Joachim   Tell me about the *Mazzot,* the 'Feast of Unleavened Bread', on the next day when the *omer,* the first sheaves of ripe barley from nearby Jericho, were brought in.

Mary   We attended the morning *Tamid* services, during which two bulls, one ram and seven one-year-old lambs were burned in atonement for sin. After that I joined the women while Joseph and Jesus joined the men, and the caravans set out for Nazareth.

As I told you earlier, we lost Jesus and we had some anxious days before we finally got on the road home. Despite the worry and anxiety, we know for certain that we are God's chosen people.

On our way we passed parties of Jews from the diaspora, as they came to have their faith strengthened by special instruction from the learned members of the Great Sanhedrin. We prayed for them in their exile and we thanked The Holy One for our simple and secure Jewish life in Nazareth.

Joachim   Blessed be God!

Is He the Messiah?

Priest, Scribe, Sadducee and Pharisee discuss the Messiah

Priest Gentlemen, thank you for coming to this unusual meeting. The reason I called you together is to talk about the future of our nation. We four, and the groups to which we belong, take our responsibility for The Holy One's governance of the nation very seriously. Our groups share a prominence which gives us power, status and some well earned income so that we can guide the ordinary uneducated people. I do not wish to look at our issues of disagreement at this time. One thing, or rather one person, has increasingly exercised our minds over the past three years. Who is this man Jesus? Some people call him a rabbi, but I believe that he is possessed.

Scribe Thank you for calling us together, despite our differences. This man has openly attacked us Scribes, telling people to beware of us and criticising our sacred robes. He does not like the fact that we have front seats in the synagogues, that we are given places of honour at banquets, or the fact that people greet us respectfully in the market place. He claims that we take money from widows. He even criticises our public prayer demonstrations and tells people to beware of us.

Pharisee It is his condemnation of our way of life that aligns us with you Scribes. He calls both of us blind guides and hypocrites. He says that we shut heaven, not allowing people to enter. He even went so far as to say that we are all fit for hell! He says that we Pharisees are dishonest about our altar offerings. More deeply, though, he fails to recognise our leadership in righteousness, when he says that if people imitate us they will never enter the kingdom of heaven.

Sadducee He aligns us also with you Pharisees when he says that both of our groups are like bad yeast. Do you remember the day we asked him for a sign to support his activity? All that he offered us was talk about Jonah being in the belly of the fish for three days, whatever that means. Then he walked away.

Of course we Sadducees have a more fundamental disagreement with this Jesus than all of you. We stand by our conviction that there is neither resurrection, nor angels, nor spirits, all three of which he speaks about frequently. But I don't want to discuss this now.

Priest   Despite any or all of our differences, may I ask if we are united about the fact that this man is leading the uneducated crowds astray? They are following him in great numbers. As the God-appointed leaders, our first question has to be: Why are people turning away from our teaching and turning to hear this carpenter from Nazareth? What is his appeal?

Scribe   Did all of you notice the type of people he has chosen to help him build this enterprise of his? His crew is made up of fishermen, tax collectors, zealots, and a few men who were unemployed. He certainly went to the edge of society to find his leaders – if we should give them that title!

Pharisee   Then he has a group of women who are constantly looking after him, a few of whom had evil spirits and other ailments. Herod's steward, Chusa, is very upset that his wife, Joanna, is one of the group. Our entire society could be undermined if women begin to find some measure of equality with men.

Scribe   You may be even more shocked to know that he talks to those women and allows them close enough to touch him. I saw them touch his arms and he did not object.

I suppose we will have to understand when Jairus, president of the synagogue, asked Jesus to cure his daughter. Jesus went with him to see the young girl and he even took her by the hand.

Then there was another case in Tyre, which we cannot condone, when he spoke to a Syro-

Phoenician woman, and then he supposedly cured her daughter.

Sadducee On another occasion he saw a crippled woman on a Sabbath, and he actually called her to his side and he cured her, despite the objections of the president of the synagogue.

Maybe we should not condemn him for helping sick women, but – I hesitate to mention it – my wife told me that when Simon the Pharisee gave a party for him, he did not object when a woman with a bad reputation, cried tears over his feet and then dried them with her hair. He could not move much closer to the margins of our society than he did in that very public act.

Priest He has been heard to say that prostitutes will get into heaven before us, the perfect people.

Talking about people on the margins, he has taken recently to befriending tax collectors and attending parties which they host for him. It may embarrass you, my Pharisee friend, to know that he told a story about one of you and a tax collector in the Temple. Both were praying, but Jesus said publicly that the tax collector was worthy, while the very prayerful Pharisee was not.

Scribe Yes, I know that the well-known tax collector, Matthew, has become one of his closest associates, and someone told me recently that Zacchaeus, the senior collector in Jericho, had fallen for his message too. Jesus claims that he addresses his words primarily to sinners. So Zacchaeus the well-known sinner then held a huge party for him, presumably inviting the usual collection of doubtful characters. The good people complained, but to no avail. Zacchaeus stood his ground.

Pharisee I heard recently that a group of mothers, without the consent of their husbands, brought their children to this Jesus to be blessed. One of his close followers, Judas, told them not to waste Jesus' time, but contrary to our tradition, he brought the children to the centre, embraced them, and blessed them, much to the delight of the foolish mothers. Children, slaves and women should be kept out of the public eye as our traditions teach.

Sadducee The latest story is that he went up to Samaria and waited at a well for a Samaritan woman who had a poor reputation. He actually asked her to give him water while they carried on a conversation. At her invitation, he stayed with her people for two full days. This man is really crossing boundaries in a serious way. He even told this woman that he is the Messiah, and that God very soon would no longer be worshipped in Jerusalem or on Mount Gerizim. It is all part of his plan to undermine the Temple of God, around which we leaders, despite our differences, are so convincingly gathered.

Priest He seems to have a preference for the foreigners too, for the Gentiles who are all definitively outsiders and sinners. He listened to the Roman centurion and cured his servant. Maybe it was because this Gentile had built the local synagogue in Capernaum and the people had requested some recognition for his generosity. They did not ask our permission. This sort of activity is outside all the boundaries of orthodoxy. The true Messiah will come to save us, his chosen people, not the Gentiles.

Scribe Yes, we have frontiers and we must guard them in the name of The Holy One who has appointed us. We have been given the one true religion and it must be protected.

Pharisee Indeed, we recite the *Shema* several times each day and we promise The Holy One our obedient listening, as his faithful ones. Sinners like the Gentiles are not descendants of Abraham our father. The publicans, the prostitutes, the lepers and the blind have forgotten their sacred ancestry, and they know nothing of The Holy One.

Sadducee There is someone knocking at the door …

Pharisee It has to be my friend and fellow Pharisee, Nicodemus. I was expecting him …

Welcome, Nicodemus. We are just concluding our meeting about this man called Jesus. We are all of the opinion that the crowds are following him because he reaches out to sinners beyond the boundaries of orthodoxy.

Priest Our High Priest Caiaphas is correct; it is better that one man die for the people than that the whole nation should perish. I know that the crowds are with him at the moment, but crowds can be fickle; Caiaphas told me privately that he has plans to work on the crowds to condemn this Jesus if we can get him arrested. He is confident about his plan and we must help him.

Nicodemus I have a confession to make; I have always been uncomfortable with condemning a man until I have heard him fully. So I went to visit Jesus on a few occasions at night. Each visit made me feel more uncomfortable still. This man brought me deeper than the Law; he spoke about life, about being born again, and about how much God loved the world.

Then I spoke to the president of the synagogue in Nazareth, who told me that when Jesus reached the age of 30, he had been invited to speak. He chose to read Isaiah, about being called to bring good news to the afflicted and to let the oppressed go free. Then he claimed that he himself was the fulfilment of this prophecy.

He compared his kingdom to a wedding banquet, and he said that those who were first invited, refused his invitation. He said the invitation is now going out to all, to everyone, everywhere, the good and the bad alike, Gentiles included.

He seemed to develop this theme when he spoke about the final judgment in which he described himself as the Son of Man spoken of by our prophet Daniel. In his mind, those saved will be those who helped the hungry, the thirsty, the naked, the stranger, the sick and the imprisoned. He does not mention those who were circumcised and faithful in Temple attendance.

Sadducee We certainly have our agencies to feed the hungry, to clothe the naked, to welcome strangers and to ensure that only the unjust are imprisoned. We have no need to hear about our obligations from an uneducated Nazarean carpenter. Can anything good come out of Nazareth?

Nicodemus   I think that in our scriptures, the word *poor* represents not only the economically impoverished but all those who are on the margin of society or excluded. And there are many forms of hunger, of thirst and of nakedness, not to mention the experience of being a stranger or an outcast. I feel sure that Jesus wants us to be more than well-intentioned social workers. He wants his followers to bring life, and to bring it abundantly to others, as he claims he himself is doing.

Priest   It is getting late. Could we bring our meeting to a close? Darkness is falling.

Nicodemus   Yes, darkness has already come.

A Father Explains

A father with two sons takes time to meet a counsellor

Counsellor   May I ask why you came to see me?

Client   Truthfully, I don't think that I need to be here at all, but my eldest son thinks that I am manifesting some strange behaviour, so I am here to make him content.

Counsellor   Could you tell me more about your situation?

Client   Maybe I can. I am a rich farm owner. Because I am a prominent man, you may have read the story in the local paper, about my son leaving home; then more recently the story of his return after many years was published.

Counsellor   Do you think the journalists got the facts or the story right?

Client   Yes, but most people lost sight of me and the depth of my feelings in the narrative. They spoke only of 'a prodigal son'. They concentrated on guilt, blame and forgiveness. Some religious groups seem to wallow in these emotions.

     Yes, I suppose my young boy behaved foolishly, but people misunderstood my true feelings. Because of this lack of insight, everyone misunderstood the deeper experience of what happened to me. Perhaps that is why my elder son sent me to you. He thinks I have become somewhat unbalanced.

Counsellor   Please tell me your own understanding of what occurred and about how you felt.

Client   Our family, like any good Jewish family, is very close. At least we were.

Counsellor   And your boy did not feel this closeness?

Client   You see, my son – he's my youngest – was always a rather impulsive fellow, and he felt inferior to his brother; he did not always act his age. One day he came to me and demanded his share of our family property in cash, and ...

Counsellor And ... ?

Client I gave it to him. I said yes, but I said it with a very heavy heart. He could see how I felt but he persisted in his demand. Of course it took a while to sell that part of the family estate, during which time I kept imploring him not to leave home. Yes, I gave his inheritance to him, reluctantly, and, of course, the family thought that I was confused, that I had made a serious error of judgement. They were all angry with me, and they could not understand why I was not as angry as they were with my son.

Counsellor And were you?

Client No, not angry, but I felt very sad, disappointed and very worried.

Counsellor You were sad about the loss of the land?

Client Maybe, just a little, but I was much more deeply saddened that my boy was leaving home. I was very concerned about his welfare, very concerned indeed. He was leaving a comfortable and loving home, with servants, good food and overall security. I was worried about what could happen to him.

Counsellor Tell me more about your sadness.

Client Well, there is not much to tell; I was very anxious, like any parent would be. I needed more time with him to heal his feelings of inferiority and of immaturity.

Counsellor Are you sure that you were not angry?

Client No, no, definitely not. How could I be angry with my son whom I love, just because he was behaving foolishly and harming himself? Being angry would be to focus only on myself.

Counsellor You tell me that you were not angry with the boy who was splitting the family estate and leaving home? Your reaction is a little unusual in the situation.

Client   No, I was not angry. You read my story. There is no mention of anger anywhere in it. Some religious people in the village claimed I was angry and that maybe I suppressed it.

Counsellor   Did you have any other feelings in the situation? Did you feel, shall we say, offended?

Client   No. As I told you, my thoughts were solely on the welfare of my boy whom I love, never on myself. I was not offended by his foolishness. You read my story. There is no mention of my son offending me. I felt sad, disappointed if you like, and very anxious about his safety and wellbeing. We Jews get on better in the country that The Holy One gave us, than in any Gentile country.

Counsellor   So you were not angry or offended; just sad, and worried about your boy's welfare?

Client   That is correct. Have you not read the interview I gave to the *Gazette*?

Counsellor   Why do you think your family is worried about you?

Client   They think that, somehow, I lost my head in allowing my son to take his share of the farm before my death, and that I allowed him to avoid the responsibility of caring for his mother and myself during our lifetime. You see, I had hoped that he would have time to grow into a mature adult before he took over his share of the home and farm.

Counsellor   But go back to your feelings if you would. How are things now?

Client   Well, my son came back recently and of course I welcomed him home. I feel very happy, very happy indeed.

Counsellor   You have another son?

Client   Yes. My elder son thinks that I should not have welcomed the younger son home. Because I did, he believes that I am more confused than ever. He thinks that I should have sent him away. That is why he says that I need counselling, even more so than before. You see, my wayward son spent all his inheritance living promiscuously, and he returned home only because he was hungry, penniless and working in a pig sty. Imagine a Jew, my son, working in a pig sty!

Counsellor   And how do you feel about his brother's reaction?

Client   Well, because I am a religious man, I knew that his reaction was not what the Most High would desire. Mercy and forgiveness – *hesed* we call it – is his permanent stance towards us, his people, despite our many infidelities. Compassion and welcome pour continuously from him. Of course I am sad too that my son cannot understand and share my feelings of joy at his brother's return.

Counsellor   Maybe he felt that you should be annoyed at his brother's rejection of your authority. Did the flaunting of your authority not annoy you? Was his disobedience not an issue for you?

Client   No, no. You must understand that, by leaving home, my son was hurting himself more than he was hurting me, and I was concerned about that most of all. Not about my authority. Besides, he came back, looking emaciated and smelling dreadfully.

Counsellor   And how did that make you feel about him?

Client   He didn't even have shoes on his feet, and his clothes were in rags. So you can imagine how I felt. Like any father would, I did not feel *about* him; I felt *for* him.

Counsellor   And why do you think your family is so worried about you?

Client   Well, I was so happy to see my boy that I ran to meet him, and I would not allow him – as tradition demands – to kiss my feet. I showered kisses on him. Yes, I was so happy that I embraced him warmly. I could feel my old heart beating against my ribs with the sheer joy of it all. I am sure he felt it too. Some of the villagers laughed at my stumbling attempt to run towards my son and welcome him home.

Counsellor   So you were really happy at his return?

Client Of course I was. I cannot understand why my elder son was so angry. He thought that I did not love him as much as I loved my younger son who went away.

Counsellor May I ask how he showed his anger towards you?

Client Well, he refused to enter the house where we were celebrating. Maybe you too will think I am confused when I tell you what I did. I gave my younger son the best robe in the house. I invited all the neighbours to our home and organized a party with music and dancing to welcome my boy back home. Much to the annoyance of my other son, I even had the calf we had been fattening for *Rosh Hashonah*, our New Year celebration, killed for the party. But I was so happy, so very happy that he had returned. I had to celebrate his homecoming.

Some religious people said that I should have given my boy a penance or at least made him promise never to do it again. But I could not. He himself offered to do penance, by becoming a hired servant. Imagine my beloved son becoming a servant in his own home. I never wanted that. I was overjoyed to see him again. That is the only feeling I had. I was jubilant.

Counsellor Are you sure?

Client Oh yes! I was a little sad when my elder son listed off his brother's sins, in public, and also when he refused to meet his brother.

I always suspected that he felt the need to earn my love, by obeying my orders and working hard. Deep down that must have made him feel like a servant. Maybe that is his problem. I have assured him again and again that all I have is his.

Counsellor Unforgiveness usually hurts the person who harbours it. How about you?

Client What do you mean?

Counsellor Well, have you forgiven your boy for his reckless behaviour?

Client I never forgave him.

Counsellor	Excuse me! Did you say that you never forgave him?
Client	That is correct. I did not need to forgive him because I had never condemned him.
Counsellor	Oh!
Client	I believe that, like many people in the village at that time, and many since then, you do not understand what happened. Where is anger, condemnation, penance or forgiveness mentioned in my interview?

Long pause

There was just deep sadness at his leaving and overwhelming joy at his return. Is that not how God our Father deals with us sinners all the time?

Counsellor	I am beginning to understand the story from your perspective as a father.
Client	When is my next appointment?
Counsellor	I think you have no need of one, but perhaps your elder son would benefit from a few visits.

A Temple Encounter

Listen to the Pharisee and the Publican at the Temple

Pharisee   Excuse me, sir, you should not enter this sacred temple. This is where The Holy One dwells and it is not a place for sinners.

Publican   Yes, I am not worthy. That is why I stayed at the rear of this holy building. I know that you were praying for people like me who you think are most in need of God's mercy. I need God's mercy so much and I trust that he will give it to me.

Pharisee   You interrupted my prayer time with the sound of your moaning and groaning.

Publican   I am sorry. I trust that God will forgive me for that too.

Pharisee   Why did you come here when you knew you were not worthy? Surely you knew that I was one of the *perusim*, the separate ones, the holy ones, who not only obey the words of the five books of the written *Torah* but also all the sacred oral traditions.

Publican   I am not a very learned man; I think I know about the *Torah* but I know nothing of the traditions of which you speak. I am sorry.

Pharisee   What do you do for a living – if you work at all?

Publican   I collect taxes.

Pharisee   I am not surprised by your choice of work since you have had no religious upbringing. You are a traitor to our nation. You work for the Romans, taking taxes from your own people. We all know your boss Zacchaeus, the senior tax collector from Jericho. He is also a no-good. I heard that he invited the travelling preacher Jesus to eat at his house. I suppose you were also there at that disgraceful gathering.

Publican   One of Jesus' followers is, or was a tax collector who worked with me. He is Levi, son of Alphaeus. You are correct. This man Jesus is rather friendly with people like me, but I have not had any invitation from him yet.

Pharisee I heard he is attracting all the ruffians and questionable characters in the country. He even accepts their invitations to share meals with them. And he eats without performing the customary washing which is laid down in the oral tradition. His disciples do the same. I am sure that they do not wash the cups, the pots or the bronze dishes either, in the way that is prescribed.

Publican Yes, I have been listening to him from time to time and I have heard your people arguing with him about these washings. He says that to wash the inside of ourselves is more important than the outside. He also said that all our rules were only human traditions, and that some leaders neglect the more important things. He said that they can even make God's word ineffective with their traditions.

Pharisee You are not only ignorant; but you are arrogant too. Yes, my friends told me about this man's opinions. He even attacked our serious practice of *corban*, of giving a gift to the Temple prior to the death of our parents. He has no respect for our authority. He is opposed to all honorific titles and he does not want anyone to have the title *rabbi*.

Publican Yes, he seems to be against all hierarchical use of power to control people. Maybe that is why people like him. We have all seen religious and civil authority abused. We tax collectors are no exception. We abuse our power by overcharging and then pocketing the unjust profits.

Pharisee Only the uninformed and uninitiated anarchists are attracted to him. Why do you not listen to us instead, and live out the traditions in every aspect of your daily life.
   I suppose you do not even recite the *Shema*?

Publican When you prayed aloud, I heard you thanking God that you were not like the rest of men. I could not pray like that. My brother told me that Jesus said we cannot pray if we do not first forgive. I have many resentments within me still. However, I take heart from what someone heard Jesus say, that he is not calling the righteous but sinners like me. Yet, some holy Pharisees follow him and he has one or two among his closest.

Pharisee   His idea of leadership is entirely different from ours. He is not selective. He looks more like a servant to me. I must get him to wash my feet sometime!

Publican   He does not seem to make distinctions, or isolate, or condemn. Even the women who look after him seem to like him. Did you hear that he even saved a woman who was caught in adultery from being stoned to death? I have not heard what happened to the man with whom she sinned, but I am sure he was not one of you *perusim*.

Pharisee   Even that thought insults us.

Publican   I heard that when Jesus invited anyone who was without sin among the accusers to throw the first stone, they all moved away silently.

Pharisee   That is what I mean; the Law has no meaning for him. No respectable man speaks to a woman, not even his wife, sister or mother, in public. That is our tradition. You remember – you probably don't – how the sages ridiculed King Agrippa for the long conversation he had with his aunt Salome.

Publican   The men of the book, the Scribes …

Pharisee   Do not suggest to me that someone like you understand the Scribes. This holy Temple is the dwelling place of God. People like you and this Jesus are like the Essene crowd in Qumran, who have no time for the Temple, its priesthood and all that it stands for. Jesus should go down to the Dead Sea and join them in their unbelief, since he claims that he is the new Temple. But I know that they would not allow either of you near their monastery.

Publican I agree with you that they would not have him with them, but for a different reason. They are too strict, too ascetical. Jesus attends parties with people you call sinners and they say that he is at his ease being close to women.

Pharisee Imagine! He says he is the new Temple and that he has neither power, status nor money. Could anything good come from the words of an uneducated carpenter?

Publican He seems to have a different kind of power, an authority about him that is without power. He seems to gather his followers by invitation, not by obligation, and from love, not from law. He invites them to join him; he does not command. A number of people are following him, especially people like me who are pushed to the margin of society and of religion. Somehow or other he has an appeal that the priests, Scribes and you people do not have. The poor, the blind and the lame – the unclean, as you call them – follow him too, since he cured some of them.

They say that he does not ask for eminence, rank or standing and that he lives out of a common purse with his close friends. One even gets the impression that he does not seem to have much time for religion, as we know it.

Pharisee He has no respect for the Sabbath, the central symbol of our religion. He and his disciples were seen plucking and chewing corn on the holy day. This confirms what you say. He has no time for our true religion.

And you? How often do you fast? Do you give tithes on your unjust earnings?

Publican You know my answer. I neither keep the fast nor give tithes. I am guilty on every level.

Pharisee My God, I thank you again that I am not like those other people: thieves, rogues, adulterers and like this Publican here.

Publican God, be merciful to me, a sinner.

Pharisee   You need to say that prayer more often.

Publican   I do not pray either, and I know that Jesus has been seen leaving the crowd quite often, to spend long periods of time alone in prayer. The crowds were looking for him to hear his words and to have their sicknesses cured, but he must have felt the need for time alone with The Holy One. What do you think that means?

Pharisee   That is enough. After speaking with you I feel the need to wash myself even more thoroughly now, before I attend our table of friendship, our *haberim*,

Publican   You are a good man; you keep the Law, but I think I will go back to hear Jesus again. One of our group, Matthew, told me that he heard Jesus say that he felt sorry for those who were harassed and helpless, like sheep without a shepherd. That describes me. Jesus also said that he was sent to call sinners and people who feel weary and who carry heavy burdens. That is me also.

Once again, I am sorry for disturbing your prayers. I am a sinner. I need to listen more deeply to the message of Jesus.

Shalom!

Light Given

A counsellor helps a blind man, sight restored, to see more clearly

Client Please excuse my awkwardness in getting around. I am slowly learning to adjust to the gift of my new-found eyesight.

Counsellor Would you like to explain?

Client Well, I was born blind. My loving parents must have been devastated when they discovered that I could not see. In a sense, I never discovered it. My experience was always one of complete darkness. Up until now I have supported myself by begging at the Temple. I was well known to many of the pilgrims, especially to those who came from my locality.

Counsellor Please tell me more about your life.

Client Being able to see now is marvellous, even though it means constant adaptation to my new world. It is like being in a new place, learning new ways of reaching out and learning to communicate differently. In other words, it is coming from total darkness into light.

Counsellor I never thought of it in that way.

Client Please try to understand my struggle.
    However, there are many other problems I would like to talk over with you.

Counsellor Yes, do feel free to speak about anything you like.

Client I have two problems. One could be described as negative and the other might be called positive.
    I will tell you about the negative one first. I have been expelled from the synagogue and my parents are constantly threatened by the Pharisees. They are frightened that they will not be able to support me. Religious leaders can be very powerful in their belief that God is always talking through them; they easily intimidate the little people like my parents.

Counsellor   And the synagogue is important to you?

Client   Yes it is. In fact, it is more important now than ever before. As you probably know, we Jews put great emphasis on purity when we worship, and somehow, a physical handicap is considered an impurity. In that way I am a sinner in the eyes of our law-abiding Pharisees.

My blindness is also blamed on my parents' sins. Pharisees called out to me, 'You were born in utter sin'. So, they say I was born blind because my parents are sinners and so I was never welcome in the synagogue and certainly not in the Temple. You can imagine my joy when my sight was restored, as I looked forward to worshipping with everyone else.

Counsellor   And you are not permitted to worship?

Client   That is correct. Lately the Pharisees are banning anyone who believes in Jesus from going to the synagogue. This gives them a second reason to exclude me. And – this will amuse you – they quizzed me so much that I could not resist asking them if they too intended to follow the man who gave me my sight. I suppose it was a cynical question, and it certainly annoyed them, because they began hurling abuse at me. When they ran out of abusive words they became quite pious, saying that they were sure God had sent Moses, but that they had no idea where this man Jesus had come from. They said that he is a sinner, and that he is possessed by a devil, because he can heal. He healed me on the Sabbath.

Counsellor   Healed you?

Client   Yes, the man called Jesus, the wandering rabbi, healed me. I did not know he was in the area; I had heard many differing opinions about him. He rarely preaches in the Temple or in synagogues. He speaks on the streets or by the lakeshore, the beauty of which I am enjoying now for the first time. The religious leaders said that he was a bad man but, regardless of that, many people continued to follow him and to listen to him.

One day as Jesus passed by my begging post, his

close followers saw me and they asked him if I or my good parents had sinned. I heard him reply that neither of us had sinned. That brought great joy to my heart.

But then he came over to me, used his saliva to moisten some mud, rubbed it on my eyes, and told me to wash it off in the pool at Siloam. One of my friends brought me there, even though he kept saying that it was a waste of time. But I did as he told me to, and now I can see. Yes, I can indeed see. My healer, Jesus, said that he was the light of the world. I do not understand that yet, but he certainly gave me light.

Counsellor   So you are very happy?

Client   Well, yes, deep down I am. You see, I have found a new reason to live. I am convinced that this good man, Jesus, is from God; maybe he is The Holy One himself.

Counsellor   Still you seem to hint that you are not entirely happy.

Client   You are correct. I am not entirely happy. In some ways I am more on the margin now than ever I was. Imagine, I am still not permitted to go to the synagogue, and people continue to point and stare at me, saying, 'He's the blind man who used to beg'. Others just cannot believe my story, and say that I merely look like the blind beggar. They are like me; they cannot believe what their eyes see, just as I found it difficult to believe what my eyes could see when I was cured.

Counsellor   Yes, all of that must be very difficult for you to cope with.

Client   Some people dragged me along to meet a group of Pharisees, and when in answer to their question, I told them exactly what happened, they said, 'This man Jesus could not be from God because he does not observe the Sabbath'. Sadly, you see, they consider that Jesus worked on the Sabbath when he made the mud paste for my healing. I disagreed with them publicly and I told them that I believe he is a prophet.

Counsellor   So, you just said what you believe.

Client   Yes, but that did not satisfy them. They came back demanding that I should give glory to God by saying that the rabbi was a sinner. My answer annoyed them even more when I replied, 'I do not know if he is a sinner. One thing I am sure of is that I was blind but now I see'. That was as simple as I could make it. I think that religion sometimes blinds people to the facts, when some of these facts do not fit easily into their system.

Now that I think about it and have talked with you, I am more at my ease; I have found the courage I need.

Counsellor   And are you still worried about your parents?

Client   They are quiet people who fear the leaders. They simply said that I was, in fact, their son and that I was old enough to speak for myself. I was sorry for them that they did not have the courage to say what I had said to them: 'Here is an astonishing thing! You know nothing about Jesus. You do not know where he comes from, and yet he opened my eyes. We know that God does not listen to sinners'. Of course they were angry about this judgement I had made of them.

Counsellor   You are a religious man and you certainly do not lack courage.

Client   Maybe in a way that is true. In my heart I do know God. Being blind and having to beg gives one plenty of time to reflect and to pray. Perhaps it was my faith or the presence of God inside me that inspired me to go back to the rabbi. I was looking for him in more ways than one. I needed to see him a second time in order to receive light in a different way.

But he was looking for me at the same time and he found me. Somehow the same longing inside both of us made us want to meet again. But I don't know for sure. Jesus did not demand that I go to the Temple,

and he said nothing about religious behaviour, but
when he heard that I was ejected from the synagogue
he found me and asked me if I believed.

Counsellor   After all that you have encountered since he healed
you, you must have been very happy to meet him
again. Do you want to tell me about that?

Client   Yes, that is the main reason I came to see you. He
asked me if I believed in the Son of Man. In our
sacred books, none of which I was able to read of
course, there is some mention of this mysterious
character. He is someone very close to God or maybe
he is the Messiah. I told him that I do believe and I
said so …

                              Long pause
Then something inside me inspired me to worship
him … and I did. I bowed down and I worshipped
him.

Counsellor   And are you totally happy now?

Client   Yes, yes. My life has changed totally and, synagogue
or no synagogue, I will surely go to hear that man
again. He gave me light in more ways than one.

Counsellor   Light?

Client   Yes, light. I suppose a different word I could use
would be 'meaning', because he gave meaning to my
life. During this talk with you, the light has become
even brighter; things have become clearer.
    Thank you for listening to me.

Counsellor   It was a joy to hear your story. I may try to hear this
Jesus myself.

Client   If you do, you will begin to see things very
differently.
    Now, pardon the pun, I can *see* myself out.

Give to the Poor

A rich young man shares his confusion

Counsellor Welcome. I like your robe and your tunic. You dress very tastefully.

Client Yes, I was taught to dress well by my parents, and besides, I am well off. In fact my Pharisee parents taught and encouraged me to do everything well.

Counsellor How can I help you?

Client I have always been a happy man and I have been truly blessed by God. Keeping God's laws – all 613 of them – is something I have done carefully since my youth. Yes, I have been blessed spiritually as well as materially.

Counsellor You seem like a man at peace with himself. Can you tell me why you made this appointment?

Client I think I can say, in all humility, that I am able to recognise goodness in another person when I see it. That is why I have been following the travelling preacher called Jesus. I feel that I have something in common with him, even though they say he does not keep every detail of the Law at all times.

Counsellor And?

Client He is a rabbi who seems to practise what he asks of others. There is something about him that makes him different. He speaks with authority and rarely refers to the oral tradition or to the *Torah* or to any of our sacred books in order to support what he speaks about. There is something authentic about him that kept me listening intently when he spoke. I believe that, like myself, he wants to please God by living a sinless life.

Counsellor Has your listening to him confused you somewhat?

Client Well, 'confused' is not quite the correct word. To say that he disturbed me a good deal and that made me feel less comfortable with my lifestyle, would be more accurate. Before I met him I was very sure of my relationship with The Holy One. As I said, I kept the Law faithfully while accumulating a lot of money through hard work and trading.

Counsellor   Would you like to tell me how he made you feel less comfortable.

Client   That is why I came to see you. I have already consulted one of the priests and two eminent Pharisees, but I did not think they were really listening to me. They seemed to want to fix me. At times I felt they just wanted to jump in with a solution. One of the Pharisees told me that the Scribes think that this man has a devil in him. Some religious people seem to think from a very fixed framework and they seem so sure of everything. Since you do not belong to any of the religious groups and you do not appear to be very religious, I thought that you might be a more objective listener.

Counsellor   Well! ... Yes, I will try.

Client   One evening recently, during my prayer time, something inside me urged me, almost forced me, to approach this man Jesus face to face after hearing one of his talks. It may seem impulsive, but I could not resist running to him, kneeling before him and addressing him as Master. The crowd gasped at my behaviour, so I said what I wanted to say immediately. I asked him what I ought do to inherit eternal life. My parents might have been annoyed if they had heard me asking him that question, because they believed with every fibre of their being that to obey the Law was the way to inherit the Kingdom. That is what they always taught me.

Counsellor   Was that what disturbed you? Could it be that you have a sort of parental fixation or is it that you have not yet become a moral adult, able to make your own choices and decisions?

Client   Not at all. Jesus confirmed what my parents had taught me. He simply gave me the answer that I already knew by heart. He listed off the

commandments of God and that made me
very happy. I was happier still, of course, to tell
him, truthfully, that I had always kept God's
commandments.

Counsellor   I am not clear then why you still felt confused.

Client   It was not his words that confused me. It was how
he looked at me. It was very clear that he admired
me and that he loved me. Oh, I could feel it, deep in
my heart. I will never forget that experience – never.
Even now I can feel it …

Counsellor   And then?

Client   Then …

Counsellor   If it is a little difficult for you to express your
thoughts and feelings just now, there is no hurry.

Client   Well, while he continued to look lovingly at me,
the Rabbi spoke again. He did not comment on my
fidelity to the Law. Clearly he approved of this.

But then he said something which shocked me. He
said that despite all my sincerity, all my efforts and
all my faithfulness, I was still lacking something. He
said that I was not perfect yet. Then he gave me an
invitation to become perfect, to be complete in a way
that I had never heard of before.

Counsellor   He made you feel sinful, guilty?

Client   No, no. He bent towards me and said that there was
a further step I could take in my effort to please The
Holy One.

Counsellor   And that was?

Client   To sell all that I have and give the money to the poor.
He invited me to come back when I had done that,
and then to become one of his close followers …

Counsellor   What did you do?

Client   Well, it took me some time to recover of this request.
I was still on my knees but feeling almost too weak to
stand up.

Counsellor   And what were your deeper feelings?

Client I felt deep confusion. Very deep confusion. You see I had already thought on a few occasions, after hearing his words while on the edge of the crowd, that I would like to join his closest followers.

But then ... very quickly I thought of all my property, my other possessions and my money, and I knew I could not say yes. I just could not. Mind you, I do give all the offerings designated by the Law to the poor, but I could not consider putting all that I own up for auction and then giving the money away.

Counsellor And your feeling? ... Guilt?

Client My feelings were very mixed as I stood up. I could not look at him. I did not want him to see my sad face. I turned away quickly and went down the alley on the left. I was holding back my tears.

Counsellor Did you feel angry that he said you could be more perfect.

Client No, just immense disappointment and immense sadness.

Counsellor And now?

Client I am still thinking about the invitation that I could see so clearly in his eyes. He spoke about having treasure in heaven, but that seems too remote when I have my treasure here and now to enjoy.

Counsellor Are you sure you don't feel guilty about refusing his invitation?

Client No, my deepest feeling is sadness at my inability to respond to his inviting eyes. Deep inside me I understand that it was an invitation to trust and to friendship that I could not respond to.

Yes, I feel a failure, not only my reluctance to let go of money and possessions but my inability to let go of myself. As I talk to you, it is becoming clearer to me that he was offering me his friendship and a deep freedom, maybe my salvation ... and I failed to accept it. Failed to say yes ... I failed.

Counsellor In what way do you think you failed?

Client   Well, friendship is about letting go, but it is also about having the freedom to part with oneself and one's possessions. I missed the chance of freedom which that good man offered me.

And it annoys me that very simple men, like fishermen, were able to leave their boats and nets and follow him. Men who did not keep the Law, like the tax collectors, were able to step away from their booths and from profitable professions. They were able to accept his liberating friendship. Rumour has it that he has built up friendship even with some women.

Now I understand that it was not about money and material things. I am not sure whether I possess the money or the money possesses me. It is so much deeper than that.

Counsellor   Deeper?

Client   Yes, the whole question of eternal life is so much deeper than just keeping the law.

Counsellor   Would you like to think more about it and come back to see me later?

Client   No, thank you. I do not need to think any more; I need time to reflect and to pray on that encounter with Jesus and on what I overheard him say to his disciples as I moved away, 'How hard it will be for those who have wealth to enter the kingdom of God'. Even his disciples looked perplexed at those words. Jesus did not withdraw or soften his words. He even added, 'It is easier for a camel to go through the eye of a needle than for someone who is rich to enter the kingdom of God'. Like his disciples, I too was astounded at what he said.

His final words encouraged me to move away from dependence on my fidelity to the Law alone: 'For mortals it is impossible, but not for God; for God, all things are possible'.

Yes, thank you for your invitation to return, but I need firstly to pause and to ponder before The Holy One.

Two Pharisees

Nicodemus and Simon share light and truth

Nicodemus   Shalom! We just have time to wash our hands before the meal.

Simon   Have you noticed that the followers of that man Jesus have continued to neglect this revered custom?

Nicodemus   Yes, it came up at the last meeting of our Council, while he was still alive. He neglected many other laws too, like speaking to women in public.

Simon   I am sure his followers do not purify their dishes.

Nicodemus   You are right. Of course, with nearly 6,000 of us Pharisees around, no disregard of the Law goes unnoticed.

Simon   Well, we, the separated ones, the elite, have done our best – not always successfully – to guard the written and the oral tradition for the last 150 years, since Jonathan made us an organized force for goodness.

Nicodemus   It's a struggle to keep all of the 613 laws all the time, but God helps us.

Simon   Talking about Jesus, I heard that he looked lovingly at one of our rich young Pharisees who said that he had kept all the laws since his youth. Some said that he invited this young ruler to join him on condition that he sold everything he had, and gave the money to the poor. Imagine! He's different, this uneducated carpenter.

Nicodemus   That is why I invited you – to talk to me about this man Jesus, since I heard that you invited him to a meal.

Simon   You never met him. And of course it is too late now because the priests have got rid of him.

Nicodemus   Yes, I did meet him but I didn't want it to be known among our friends. I went to see him one night.

Simon   My curiosity gave me a bit more courage than you. I invited him to an open meal one day, but I messed up a potentially fruitful encounter. My courage wavered when I noticed that my other guests were watching me. I did not offer him the usual ritual welcome, like water on his feet, oil on his head and a kiss. As it turned out, this lack of courage and lack of courtesy was a mistake. He was hurt. Tell me about your own meeting with him.

Nicodemus   I was more than curious, as I watched what he did: I was standing on the edge of the crowds listening to him. Something inside me was telling me that God was with this man. As a teacher in Israel, I had always felt the obligation to learn, to listen, as well as to talk. I have always been a bit of a searcher, you know.

Simon   Did you learn much during your visit?

Nicodemus   Although he confused me at the beginning by talking about being born again, I certainly did learn. If I am honest, it was even deeper than that. I was a changed man. He did not put as much emphasis on the Law as we do. Instead, he went much deeper, by talking about God's love as primary motivation. He spoke also about light and about truth. He seemed to be inviting me to trust him as a manifestation of God, and as a mediator of God's eternal life. It was deep water …

Simon   What is that about light and truth? The Psalmist tells us that God's Law is a light for our feet and a truth for our hearts.

Nicodemus   I'm not too clear yet about all that he said but there is something inside me drawing me forward to understand it more fully. It seems to be changing me gradually. He did say something about a spirit blowing around us and inside us, like the wind.

Simon   It sounds all very vague to me. Like yourself, I was brought up with stress on behaviour as the sole measure of our relationship with God. As you know, the thrust of our whole tradition has been to resist new ideas, innovations and foreigners. Keep to the sacred rituals and ordained feasts, I always said. From the time of the Greek conquest of our country, and even before it – and that is a long time ago – we have been sure of our tradition, as we sing in the Psalm: 'How I love your law'.

Nicodemus I know that Jesus called us blind guides, hypocrites and even fools. Hearing a good man say these things made me keep searching. Could he be right or even partially right? As I purify my dishes at home I am reminded that he said we are like people who wash only the outside of the dish. He accused us of being full of greed and wickedness.

Simon I heard that he was critical of us for taking the seats of honour in the synagogue and for expecting special greetings in the marketplace. You told me once that you were never comfortable about taking those front seats, and having people bow to you as you passed by.

Nicodemus He included us with the Scribes, one of whom said he was insulting them too. He challenged them that they were loading people with burdens that were hard to bear. The Scribes joined a few of my friends who soon became very hostile towards him. They kept trying to catch him in something he might say, and Naaman asked me to join them. However, by then I was beginning to see some truth in what the man was saying, and I was feeling a strange attraction towards him.

Simon A good friend of mine says that Jesus called us a brood of vipers and said that we close the gates of heaven against people. Rough stuff!

And he was not careful about Sabbath observance either. He defended his friends who plucked and cleaned corn on the holy day. He ended that encounter by saying – I hope I quote him correctly – 'What I want is mercy, not sacrifice'. Something inside me, like that wind or breeze you spoke about, keeps that phrase spinning around in my head.

Nicodemus A few days ago, our Council had to deal with a young Pharisee called Saul. He charged impetuously into our meeting and talked loudly about killing all the followers of this Jesus. We calmed him down but I have a feeling that he has not changed much. There are some in the Council who may encourage him still. He will have to be watched.

Simon   I am a little confused about the whole situation. The number of his followers is growing, especially among the tax collectors, prostitutes and sinners in general. He reached out, going towards the people on the margins of society and of what we call religion. He even ate with publicans and sinners. Of course, I did not know this before I invited him to my place. You understand?

Nicodemus   I have a confession to make. I tried to save him and I buried him ...

Simon   You what?

Nicodemus   You were not at the Council meeting when I spoke up. The council members ganged up with the priests and we sent guards to record what this innovator was preaching. We nearly tore our garments when they came back saying, 'No one has ever spoken like this'. Some of the Council said, 'So, have you too been led astray? Have any of us come to believe in him?' Isaac called his followers a rabble.

I saw that things were getting out of hand so I quietly reminded the Council that we could not pass judgement until we gave Jesus a hearing ourselves. They were angry and they then attacked me also, saying, 'Are you too a Galilean?', reminding me at the same time that prophets never came from Galilee.

Simon   And you said that you buried him?

Nicodemus   As you can guess now, I slowly became one of his disciples. So did another Council member, Joseph of Arimathaea. When they took him down from the cross, I brought a king's weight of myrrh and aloes to anoint his body. Then Joseph and I and some women friends of his buried him.

Simon   I also have a confession to make. During our meal with Jesus, a prostitute who admired him came in.

She let her hair down and anointed his feet while she shed tears. Of course, we all gasped and I objected. But Jesus said – this time I remember the words well – 'Her many sins have been forgiven; hence she has shown great love'. Lest there was any ambiguity, Jesus continued: 'But the one to whom little is forgiven, loves little.'

Nicodemus Yes, that is the Jesus I know now. His risen Spirit in my heart tells me that we meet God by recognising that we are sinners and that we are mercifully loved by him. Only then do we love him spontaneously.

Simon If you are saying that we do not earn God's love by keeping the Law and that being loved comes before loving, then something in me – again that breeze you spoke of, that spirit – makes me want to believe it.

Nicodemus The night on which we met was both confusing and challenging for me, Simon.

Jesus' central message was about being re-born – which I mistakenly took for re-entry into one's mother's womb. I said this and he replied, 'What is born of the flesh is flesh, and what is born of the Spirit is spirit.' This new birth was clearly a gift from above, to be received in faith. It involved a human experience with water and an otherworldly experience of the Spirit which, like the breeze, is beyond human control. He spoke about seeing the Kingdom of God, and then about entering it. I felt that I was being invited into the Mystery of The Holy One, without any mention of the Law.

Simon I am perplexed because I believe that we are being invited away from our own categories, into heavenly things, into the mysterious life of the Spirit.

Nicodemus I think we should reflect on and look more deeply into our experiences of this man. Could we meet with our friend Joseph in Arimathea – just two or three of us together, as Jesus said.

Simon And maybe, we could invite our rich young friend whom Jesus admired when he said that he had kept every tittle of the Law. He would gladly have us to his home and give us a good meal. We all need to listen to that spirit within us.

Simon, am I asking too much if I suggest that we invite that woman who came into your dining room to meet Jesus?

Nicodemus I am sure that the young man would be interested in our invitation. But your suggestion about the woman? Perhaps, on another occasion!

Goodness Confused

The Samaritan tells his counsellor,
'No, I did not leave him.'

Counsellor	Welcome, Sir. You look a little upset.
Client	Upset? Indeed I am.
Counsellor	Can you explain to me what you think it is that causes your discomfort?
Client	Well, I feel that I am marginalized by those who know me in the town, and my friends say that I need some counselling.
Counsellor	Can you tell me how you are marginalized?
Client	I am a simple man and I have lived happily with my family for many years. I trade quietly in water, salt, fruit, oil and dried fish, along the road from Jericho to Jerusalem. It is a demanding life. I have to give regular bribes to the bandits and, because of that, my profits are reduced. It is hard work for my donkey, especially when we are going uphill towards Jerusalem. So here I am, in need of some advice.
Counsellor	I can help you to reflect on your life and resolve your feelings so that you can find peace of mind. However, we counsellors do not give advice. Now, where do you feel you would like to begin?
Client	You may or may not understand that there is great enmity between the Jews and us. I am a Samaritan. The tension is all about whether we ought to worship on Mount Gerizim or on Mount Zion in Jerusalem, and about how we should interpret the sacred books. I do not fully understand it all, but our rabbis accept only the first five scrolls with Joshua and Judges while the rabbis in Jerusalem accept many more. Deeper still, it is about who can be described as a true Israelite.
Counsellor	It sounds very complicated. Can you help me to understand what makes you feel so upset about it all?

Client   Well, first of all, I am not a very religious man, and all this disagreement about places to worship and how to understand books, is well beyond my capacity to understand. The Holy One did not gift me with a high intelligence.

Counsellor This all seems to be a serious matter for the religious people in your village. Why has it affected you? How are you caught up in all of this?

Client   Yes, 'caught up' is a good description, but I had to tell you about the place I live in to help you understand the situation.

Counsellor I am still not clear what all this has to do with your peace of mind and your feelings, and of course, you understand that I cannot fix religious divisions or make moral judgements. However, I can perhaps help you with your feelings. Tell me about these.

Client   Well, this is how it all began. I was riding my donkey down that very steep road from Jerusalem back to Jericho. I stopped to give the donkey a rest and to have a drink. As I sat there, all the Samaritans who passed by said, 'Shalom', but the Jews just glanced at me as they passed. A priest and a Levite passed too, without even turning their faces to look at me. But I understood why they did not salute me. They were hurrying to reach their place of worship in Jerusalem. Religious duties are so important. After resting my donkey, I continued downwards on my journey.

Counsellor And?

Client   Just a short distance further down the road, I saw a man lying naked on the roadside. He had obviously been attacked by the bandits and had been stripped of all his belongings. Maybe, for all I know, they were Samaritan bandits who attacked him. The priest and the Levite must have seen him too, but I am sure that because they were on their way to lead the religious services they could not stop to help him.

   The man must have tried to resist the brigands, because he was battered and bleeding. My first inclination was to look away and pass on. The religious teaching of my childhood spoke about hating strangers, and about becoming impure by touching blood. It all came back to me, making me hesitate to offer any assistance to the poor man. All my natural inclinations were telling me not to speak to him and not to touch him, because it was not I who had harmed him ...

Besides that, I was on my way to meet a friend who might give me a permanent job in Jericho.

Counsellor And?

Client Well, I was torn between following my head or my heart. No ...

It was even deeper than my heart; it was in the pit of my stomach that I felt pain for the unfortunate man. I felt more than pity; I felt compassion for him; I felt his pain.

I knew that the priest and the Levite had passed him for religious reasons. Their religion, like mine, forbids them to touch blood or corpses. And, like me, they were not sure if he was a Samaritan or a Jew. But I could not walk away. My deepest feeling would not allow me ...

I somehow felt the man's misfortune inside myself. There was a voice, a feeling, in me telling me to dismount and help ease this man's suffering.

Counsellor What sort of a feeling was it? Maybe many feelings?

Client First of all, it was fear. I was afraid that some of the bandits, unknown to me, would return to attack me too. But I also felt stressed about choosing between what my traditions had taught me, and my own fellow-feeling for the injured man.

Anyhow, I did dismount and I approached the man who I feared might be dead. I poured some healing oil on his wounds, tore some old clothing into strips, then I bandaged him to stop the bleeding.

Counsellor And you hoped that he would survive after you left him?

Client No, I did not leave him. I lifted him on to my donkey and brought him to the inn where I left him until the following day. You remember I had that appointment with my friend about the job. By the way, I did get the job, and the loan of some money also.

When I returned to the inn on the following evening, the innkeeper asked for two denarii to cover the cost of the poor man's stay. That was the equivalent of two days' wages for most people, but I paid him. He and I were both very happy to see how much the wounded man had improved.

Counsellor Very happy?

Client Yes, very happy indeed, until the innkeeper let it slip to one of my townspeople that I had rescued and paid for the care of an injured Jew. Now, many of my townspeople reject me since they heard that news, because the injured man worships in Jerusalem.

Counsellor So you are sorry now that you got involved with the Jew at all?

I mean, do you regret it?

Client Not really, but I feel the pain of rejection by some of my close friends.

Counsellor Any other feeling?

Client I am a little sad for my friends who cannot feel compassion and practise active concern for strangers in distress. I think that I feel a little angry at the priest and the Levite who thought that their religious duties were more important than the practical care of someone in need.

Counsellor Any deeper feelings?

Client Yes. I have. Now that I have talked with you, I have a good feeling about myself. I believe that I have moved out of my prison of prejudice. At the same time I have also escaped from being controlled by any negative feelings of discomfort when I show love to someone in need. It is a great feeling of freedom. Yes, the freedom to love. Maybe it is like The Holy One.

Counsellor A religious feeling?

Client   Not really, it is just a human feeling, that is, unless being religious includes helping your enemy. Of course I still wonder how, and indeed why, the priest and the Levite passed the wounded man. Maybe one can be too religious, especially if one is part of the religious elite. There is a rumour too that this Jesus cured ten lepers and that only one of them returned to thank him – one of ours, a Samaritan.

As in all of life, the religious lines are getting crossed and some people do not like it. They then compare faith to membership of a club, in which you must keep all the rules or you are out.

Counsellor   I still do not understand the religious side of your problem but it may help if I tell you that a previous client told me that this travelling teacher called Jesus seems to have great concern for people in need and that he is very close to God at the same time. So maybe your concern for others is not too far removed from true religion.

Client   I am so glad that you mentioned the man Jesus. A friend of mine told me that Jesus heard about my good deed to the injured man and that he described it to one of the Scribes – they are the experts on the Law – who had asked him what was the first of all the commandments. My friend said that, when the Scribe persisted in asking Jesus who was his neighbour, he told him always to do what I had done for a stranger in need of assistance.

I am beginning to see that it depends on how you define the word 'religion'. As I told you, I am not a very religious man but maybe The Holy One is moving me beyond the boundaries that made me feel marginalized in the village. Could it be that God has no margins to his love?

Counsellor   Sorry, but I cannot help you to resolve your religious scruples. If you need another appointment, please let me know.

Client   Before I go, may I ask for a little advice? I have thought of moving to another Samaritan town called Sychar. What do you think?

Counsellor   We counsellors usually do not give advice about decisions like that, but since you have regained your confidence I cannot see any reason why you should move away from your own town. Would your work not suffer, and your family? And of course, you would be a stranger in Sychar.

Client   Well, I have some relatives there. One of them is called Aquila who met this Jesus at Jacob's well and she gave him a drink. It is difficult to believe but she said that she had a long conversation with him.

Then she left her water jar, hurried back to the town, and excitedly invited the people of the town to listen to him. Many of them did go to hear him and he accepted their invitation to stay for two days, but the rabbis rejected him. Aquila told me that it is a very religious town also, where the rabbis believe that they have all the answers because they have all the power.

Of course, we all know that Jesus should not have been speaking to Aquila. The religious people regard her as a bad women because she married more than once. That is why she has to go to the well alone, and at the hottest time of the day. In our religion, a second marriage means that you are out of the synagogue. There is no margin for mistakes in our religion!

Counsellor   Again, I am sorry that I do not have any useful guidance for you on this subject but let me know if you would like another appointment for further counselling.

Client   Thank you, but I think I need my next appointment to be with that travelling rabbi, Jesus.

A Celebrating Sinner

Zaccheus discusses his new way of life

Counsellor   You are the local tax-agent, are you not?

Zacchaeus   Yes, that is who I am. In fact, I'm the top man in charge of all the tax-agents.

Counsellor   It is difficult to be popular then, I presume?

Zacchaeus   By Jove, that is for certain. At least, up until now. That is why I have come to see you. I am no longer sure how people feel about me but, more especially, where I am inside myself. You might say that I have what they call an identity crisis. I need to talk to you.

Counsellor   So you are feeling somewhat confused?

Zacchaeus   I have so many mixed feelings all at once since the time I changed. Or should I say *was* changed?

Counsellor   Could you try to name some of your feelings?

Zacchaeus   Well, the guilt is still with me because of past greed, and I have a feeling of loneliness too, because I have no real friends. Then, of course, fear is always present lest I am killed or robbed by a Zealot when working at my booth.

Counsellor   That is a great range of feelings, Sir.

Zacchaeus   And that is not all of them; there are more. Recently underneath all these bewildering feelings I am becoming very happy because of what happened to me. Wait a moment – let me correct that – it is what has happened *in* me. Yes, by Jove, it is what happened *in* me.

Counsellor   Could we try to look at these feelings one by one?

Zacchaeus   Yes, I would surely like to try. You see the Romans rent out the tax-collecting business and they give us protection. We pay the rent and after that we can keep whatever we can squeeze out of the people. Then, as the local *capo*, I get a slice from each agent under me. Yes, I am a wealthy man.

Counsellor   And as you said, you are still feeling guilty too.

Zacchaeus   Up until now I rarely felt guilty. My parents taught me to be realistic and enterprising. So I knew that being a tax-agent was a good job. But with the many people whom I have hurt strewn behind me, I do feel very guilty now.

Counsellor   I think I can guess why you feel unpopular, unwanted and lonely.

Zacchaeus   Mind you, I have people whom I call friends among the other tax collectors. We stick together and we meet often to celebrate. Wine, women and song, you understand? Not religious songs! 'Wine makes your heart rejoice', as the religious people say in the Psalm. And of course, we pay the girls well. But, as you might expect I never go to the synagogue and rarely to the Temple. So culturally, socially and religiously I am on the edge, unwanted and even hated.

Counsellor   I think you said that you live with a lot of fear too.

Zacchaeus   You can imagine. The Zealots sneak around with short daggers under their dirty cloaks, not only looking for the backs of some drunken Roman soldiers but for us collaborators, as they call us. I have to keep my eyes moving continually in all directions when I am in the street, and I certainly keep out of the souks. Then, as you can see, I am neither tall nor strong.

Counsellor   You mentioned that recently you have become happier, even though the residue of some negative emotions remains.

Zacchaeus   I remember well. It was a very warm day as only Jericho can be warm. Word got around that the miracle-worker, Jesus from Nazareth, was approaching the town. Nearly half the people went out to get a look at him. Initially, I was curious too, especially because I heard that my former colleague Matthew was among his closest friends.

Counsellor   Matthew?

Zacchaeus   Yes, Matthew was also a tax agent. As I was saying, after the town's people had gone out, my curiosity drove me out alone to see this Jesus. When I saw the crowd approaching with Jesus I felt afraid. Anyway, I could not get near him, and I dared not go into the crowd lest I get knifed. Someone told me that Simon the Zealot was one of this Jesus' close friends. So I knew that I had to keep my distance.

Counsellor   So, did you stay on the edge of the crowd or go home?

Zacchaeus   No, no, not at all. Enterprise is my middle name. Something inside me was telling me that I *must* see this Jesus. I went back up the road and I scrambled up a sycamore tree. You know those trees with the big wide leaves. I positioned myself to be invisible to the crowd, as I hoped, but with a view. Then I waited as they approached.

Counsellor   Why were you so willing to look foolish by climbing a tree?

Zacchaeus   I told you. First of all it was curiosity but gradually it was something inside me that made me take the risk. Maybe I could describe it as a religious experience. I just had to see that man.

Counsellor   And the crowd passed by.

Zacchaeus   No, and that is the beginning of my real story. Jesus stopped the crowd and looked straight up at me. My heart started thumping! Some of the crowd began shaking their fists up at me. And there was more to come. Jesus called me by my name. Can you imagine that? 'Zacchaeus', he said, 'come down' …
Long pause
Imagine that – he called me by name …
Long pause
By Jove!

Counsellor   And you came down?

Zacchaeus   No. I did not. I was too afraid. Many of my enemies were in that crowd.
    Then Jesus called me again, and this time he said,

'Hurry down, for I must stay at your house today'...
Long pause
I particularly recall his words 'I must'. I thought of
how I had felt at the toll booth, that I must go to see
him. There was already something inside both of us,
something pushing both of us to meet. There was ...
Long pause

Counsellor   Can you say what it was?

Zacchaeus   For me it was a very deep and overpowering feeling.
Maybe it was somewhat like I felt at my *Bar Mitzvah*
but this time it was much richer. Much richer. It just
took me over.

Counsellor   And is that what has made you happy?

Zacchaeus   No, not entirely. First of all, it was the feeling that
this good man, Jesus, was accepting me without
reservation. He did not name all the things I did
wrong nor did he tell me what a traitor and playboy
I was. He did not even ask me to straighten out my
life nor to repent, as the John the Baptiser demanded
from his followers.

Counsellor   So you felt totally accepted, after being rejected for so
long.

Zacchaeus   Yes, with no finger-pointing, no conditions, no
confessions and no promises, he chose me. He asked
to visit my home, and to have a meal together – the
house of a sinner as the religious people described it.
A shared meal just for friendship is very significant
in our culture. He sat down with the other tax
collectors and some questionable characters at my
table. Naturally, I sat between Jesus and Matthew. Of
course, we did not bring in the girls on that occasion.

But it was great, just great. I welcomed him
joyfully, and he was very happy too. All the holy
people who attend the synagogue every Saturday
were grumbling about his going to stay in the house
of a man who is a sinner.

Counsellor   I presume that they were outside your house and
noisy. Did this bother you?

Zacchaeus   No, I stood my ground. I was a new man. I decided to give up my wrongdoing, and right there I promised before all my friends that I would give half of my money to the poor. As the Law commands, I also agreed to repay fourfold anyone whom I had cheated.

Counsellor   So being accepted was the beginning of a new experience for you.

Zacchaeus   Indeed it was a new experience, a new life. I was so happy that I felt free to give away half of my possessions and to fulfil the strictest law about repaying fourfold what I had taken unjustly. I used to laugh at John the Baptiser who told us tax-agents to collect no more than the amount prescribed.

Now you understand that I really confessed my sins and changed my life after I got the communion of friendship. In other words, communion led me to confess and to change. The priests and the Pharisees teach that one must confess and change one's life first before being accepted into the Temple ceremonies.

Counsellor   And that removed much of the guilt?

Zacchaeus   Yes, I felt like a new man, with a new fullness of life. You see, deep down I realized that I was searching for salvation from my own selfishness all my life. Now this man of God was really seeking me, but I did not know it.

Counsellor   So you are happy to be poor now.

Zacchaeus   No, Jesus did not ask me to give all my wealth away – at least not yet anyway. In fact he did not ask me to give up anything. It was his acceptance and his love for me that induced me to give up so much. It was love which moved me; it was not demand or diktat. He seemed happy that I kept half of what I owned.

Counsellor   This religious experience made you very happy?

Zacchaeus   Jesus did not mention religion as I know it. He certainly did not mention Temple worship or synagogue attendance. But I know that when things settle I will turn up there from time to time. He said only that salvation had come to my house. And, by Jove, it has. I am a free man. Now I will have to stop swearing by the Roman god, Jove or Jupiter.

Counsellor Has our talking about it helped you?

Zacchaeus Yes, Sir! Indeed it has. I've discovered that I am truly a free man, a free man!

But I must give you a laugh before I go. The derivation of my name Zacchaeus means 'the innocent one', 'the clean one'. By Jove! What do you think of that? ...

And oh! by the way, don't forget to send the bill.

A Revelation

Conversations among the disciples at the Last Supper

Peter James, what is he going to do with a basin of water and a towel ?

James He is going to wash your feet.

Peter Lord, are you going to wash my feet ?'

Jesus You do not know now what I am doing, but later you will understand.

Peter You will never wash my feet.

Jesus Unless I wash you, you will have no share with me.

Peter Lord, not my feet only but also my hands and my head !

James John, he is approaching me now and I am bewildered. You and I remember the vision on the mountain and the voice from the clouds proclaiming, 'This is my well beloved Son.' If our ambitious mother saw this, she too would be confused about her hope that Jesus had thrones, and about the chance of my going to high places with him. Here he comes on his knees and I must hurry to slide off my sandals. I am very confused. *Boanerges* or sons of thunder as he called us, are very quiet now!

John Thomas, what I am seeing cannot be true – the person whose presence among us fulfils the Law and the Prophets, and who is the new Temple, is about to wash my feet. I know that he loves me and my name John means 'God is gracious'. Perhaps this is the graciousness of God – God as my servant. Could this be the meaning of what we are witnessing and experiencing?

And notice, Thomas, that my feet are covered in the dried mud from the puddle I stepped into in the darkness on the street. Perhaps you did not know that he asked Peter and myself to prepare this

Passover meal for our community, and I did not
have time to take a bath. He will have a difficult
time washing.

Thomas Philip, I cannot believe what I am seeing. I recall
that on our way to Lazarus' home I said, 'Let us go
and die with him', and then followed it by my deep
doubts about his resurrection. If he knows all things,
he knows about my vacillations between courage
and doubt, and yet he is coming to wash my feet.
How can I look into his eyes if he looks up at me?
At this moment I feel like slipping away quietly and
going back to my home in Bethsaida.

Philip Thomas, I understand how you feel, but you cannot
steal away at this moment.

Now, I have a different problem. I've always
thought of myself as a practical man, and as one
who was capable of assessing the cost of bread to
feed a large crowd, and courageous enough to point
out to Jesus the madness of trying to feed so many
on the other side of the lake. However, I am not
quite at my ease with Jesus when we are close up.
When the Greeks told me that they wanted to speak
to Jesus, I had to get Andrew to come with me. I also
recall how all his talk about the Father made me ask
to see him. 'Philip,' he said, 'Have I been with you so
long and yet you do not know me?

Once again I am about to meet him face to face
at another embarrassing moment, when he is sure
to look through me. Now I ask myself, who is going
to wash my feet? Can this Palestinian carpenter
be truly God, The Holy One? I feel anxious, very
anxious indeed.

Bartholomew Andrew, I wonder if this points to a new type of
leadership in Jesus' community. I cannot imagine
any of the High Priests or Scribes, much less Herod
or Pilate, going around on their knees washing
anybody's feet. That is surely the duty and action
of a pagan slave. If this is a new style of leadership,
not many will choose it. It might be called power-
on-its-knees. He cannot expect many vocations or
followers unless the movement changes. We all like

to move upwards, in our career choices. Oh, it is coming closer to my turn.

Andrew
Matthew, you saw how my brother Peter has already annoyed Jesus by his refusal to have his feet washed. I certainly do not want to repeat that scene. To our great discomfort he said that all of us will be dragged before Sanhedrins and beaten in the synagogues. He also told us not to be concerned if we are brought before governors and kings for his sake.

The word 'worry' does not seem to be in his vocabulary. I suppose we can only trust without fear when we do not understand what he is asking of us, and this washing of my feet is certainly one of those moments for me.

Matthew
Andrew, this sort of thing never went on at my booth; it was all business with the help of the two soldiers given to me by the Romans. If any Zealot saw a Jew washing my feet, he would kill him. And if my father Alphaeus or any of my workmates saw someone, anyone, washing my feet, they would laugh me out of business.

If Jesus in some way represents the God of creation or is to be identified with the God of Sinai then his serving us in the form of a slave is the very opposite of what our Scriptures have told us. They so often stress that our lives are to be spent serving God according to the Law. We were told that we are made to know, love and to serve him. Now, we are encountering God who is loving and serving us.

Andrew
Matthew, yes, it is a new experience of God for all of us.

Matthew
Andrew, of course I remember that he condemned leaders who wield authority over others, and I recall the strange words he used about his having come, not to be served by us, but rather to serve us. He is certainly about to do it to me right now.

It helps me that I once heard him say that he loves us like a mother hen loves her chicks. He is coming closer. I must remove my dirty sandals.

Simon
Thaddeus, you are a peaceful man, but it has been

my conviction that the only way to get the Romans
out of our land is by force, so I joined the Zealots.
Jesus has convinced me otherwise, especially when
he said that those who live by the sword die by the
sword.

Now that I see him on his knees washing other
people's feet, it reminds me of his telling us that he
is 'gentle and humble of heart'. Did I believe it? I
am not sure that I am prepared to wash people's feet
beyond those of my parents whose feet I kissed so
often. It will certainly be news around Galilee if I am
seen doing it. My former comrades will wonder what
has happened to tough, dagger-wielding Simon. They
will surely laugh at me, maybe kill me.

Thaddeus Simon, I wonder if this is not connected to some
kind of central ritual which he might leave us to re-
enact together. In our Scriptures The Holy One told
us to love our neighbour as ourselves, but this very
night Jesus told us to love one another as he loves us.

The standard of loving has changed. Jesus' loving
is not just avoiding hurt to one another; it looks like
a very humble service. If his movement establishes
this foot-washing of one another it would certainly
signify the sincerity of our togetherness, and test us
every time we worship together.

James Judas, have you noticed that Jesus is not speaking?
Son of He is saying nothing. He is giving a very quiet and
Alphaeus a very visual message. I wish he explained it to me
before I feel his strong carpenter's hands massaging
my feet as he washes them.

Judas I have watched him shuffle along with his basin and
to himself towel. I have watched the puzzled faces of the men,
and now he is nearly at my feet. This performance
convinces me that I have made a sensible decision to
get out of this movement.

In fact, something inside possesses me, and it is
helping me to deepen that decision. I will look down
at him washing my feet. I pity and despise him with
his religious nonsense and his vague talk about the
Father, and about a new life here and hereafter, and
a kingdom where the king washes people's feet. He

already knows that I have sold him, and I can touch the 30 coins in my purse. I feel like leaving the room after this performance but my departure would be too obvious. I will stay until the Passover meal is over when it is dark. I will feel more comfortable in the darkness.

Jesus Do you know what I have done to you? You call me Teacher and Lord, for so I am. If I, then, your Lord and Teacher, have washed your feet, you also ought to wash one another's feet. For I have given you an example, that you also should do as I have done to you.

I give you a new commandment – that you love one another; just as I have loved you, you also should love one another. By this, everyone will know that you are my disciples, if you love one another.

Peace I leave with you; my peace I give to you. I do not give you as the world gives.

Do not let your hearts be troubled, and do not let them be afraid. You heard me say to you, I am going away and I am coming to you. Believe in God. Believe also in me. In my Father's house there are many dwelling places. I go to prepare a place for you. I will come again and will take you to myself, so that where I am you may be also. You know where I am going.

Thomas Lord, we do not know where you are going. How can we know the way?

Jesus I am the way, and the truth, and the life. No one comes to the Father except through me. If you know me, you will know the Father also. From now on, you do know him and you have seen him.

Philip Lord, show us the Father and we will be satisfied.

Jesus Have I been with you all this time, Philip, and you still do not know me? Do you still not understand, that whoever has seen me has seen the Father.

Rise, we must be on our way.

A Locked Room

Safety in numbers for eleven scared men

Andrew   Is the room locked, Peter?

Peter   Yes, I locked it; but check it again. Bartholomew, you are near the door. Let us know if you hear any noise outside.

Jude   My father told me that he thinks it is not over yet. He feels sure that the Temple is determined to wipe us out. He did not want me to come with you, reminding me that I am not one of the Twelve anyway.

Thaddeus   It has all been a terrible experience since that night in the garden. I know I was the first to get away but when I saw that Peter had brought a sword, after all Jesus said about violence, I knew that he was expecting trouble. What happened after I left?

Philip   We all followed you, and I noticed that John and Peter followed the arresting cohort with Jesus, at a distance.

John   Yes, I had met the High Priest a few times, so he let me into the palace. I could not convince Peter to come in.

Peter   Indeed. Now I wish I had. Then I would not have met that inquisitive young woman who recognised me as a follower of Jesus while I was sitting by the charcoal fire. And now I have a confession to make. I denied, three times, that I knew Jesus. Just then they were dragging him across the courtyard and he looked straight at me … I remembered that he told me he was going to suffer grievously at the hands of the elders, the chief priests and the scribes, and be put to death. But you know how impetuous I am. That maid's remark made me think of my own skin. I cursed and swore that I did not know him. And Jesus called me *kepha*, a rock … in truth I was more like mud.

John I must add something to that for myself, for Peter and for James. Some time ago, Jesus took the three of us up a mountain and he was revealed to us in splendour with Moses and Elijah. We heard a voice from heaven declaring him to be the beloved Son of God. On the way down, he forbade us to speak about this privilege until he has risen from the dead. I was so overwhelmed by the vision that it is only now I recall these words, 'risen from the dead', but I'm still wondering what they mean.

Matthew Some of you have the luxury of religious guilt, but I have a real problem. I'm now an unemployed and disliked ex-taxcollector. I can never get the job back. I'll be despised more than ever all over Galilee. Most of you can go back to fishing with your family. I heard that old Zebedee is finding it difficult since James and John left him so suddenly.

Philip When Jesus was arrested, didn't he say, 'Let these go'? Maybe he did not mind our running away.

Bartholomew But when he called you and me on that street in Bethsaida he did say, 'Follow me'. And at our final meal I will never forget what he said when you asked to see the Father. He said to you, 'Anyone who has seen me has seen the Father'. And. Philip, you inspired him to feed the large crowd that had followed us to the other side of the lake. You seemed at ease when asking him to do things. You were close to him.

Simon I wonder will my Zealot friends ever forgive me for deserting the struggle against the Roman oppressors. I have even given away my precious dagger.

My deepest memory will always be the moment he washed my dirty feet; I can never forget that. And I was only half awake in the garden, to hear him say, 'You can sleep on now and have your rest. It is all over. The hour has come'. If I had had my dagger at that time, I might have used it on Judas after he kissed the Master.

Andrew Several of you will recall the day, while sitting on the Mount of Olives, that we heard him talk about how it would happen that not a single stone of the great Temple will be left on another, that everything will be pulled down. He said that we will be handed over to the Sanhedrin, and beaten in the synagogues, but that we should not worry. I remember too that he said, 'Anyone who stands firm to the end will be saved'. It all sounds very real and uncomfortable now. Is this the end?

Peter I heard that a secret disciple, called Joseph, asked Pilate for the body, and that it was a Pharisee who gave him a burial place. Was anyone there on Calvary with him at the end?

James Yes, John was there with Mary, his mother, with Magdalen and with some other women. It must have been difficult for Mary to see her flesh and blood nailed to that cross and then to watch them cast lots for his tunic which she had so beautifully woven in one piece.

Peter Where is John now?

All He is in the next room with Mary. I will call him. No, he is coming in.

John Mary and I stayed until he died. I have not much to say. It was terrible, terrible.

Peter Would Mary like to speak?

John No! Gasping for breath in his dying moments, Jesus first forgave his killers. He asked me to care for his mother and assured me that she would be my mother now. Then he cried out in desperation, ' My God, my God, why have you forsaken me?' And his final words were, 'Into your hands I commend my spirit'.

Bartholomew Listen, there is a gentle knock at the door ... Through the cracks I can see it's Mary of Magdala. I will let her in.

Magdalen The Lord is risen, and I have seen him. He called my name, and after asking me not to cling to him he said, 'Go to my brothers, and tell them that I am ascending to my Father and to your Father, to my God and to your God'.

Peter   That sounds like so much nonsense.

Bartholomew   What is that strange sound?

Peter   Look, It is the Lord!

All   Master!

Mary   My son!

Magdalen   Rabunni!

Jesus   Peace be with you! Why are you so frightened and why do these doubts arise in your hearts? Look at my hands and my feet; see, it is I myself. Touch me and see; for a ghost does not have flesh and bones as you see that I have.

Everything about me in the Law of Moses, the prophets and in the Psalms must be fulfilled. It is written that the Messiah is to suffer and to rise from the dead on the third day, and that repentance and forgiveness of sins is to be proclaimed in his name to all nations. You are witnesses to these things.

And see I am sending you what the Father promised; so stay here in the city until you have been clothed with power from on high. As the Father sent me, so I am sending you. Receive the Holy Spirit. Go, make disciples of all nations. Baptise them in the name of the Father and of the Son and of the Holy Spirit, and teach them to observe all the commands I gave you. And, look, I am with you always; yes, to the end of time.

A day later

Peter   Welcome back, Thomas. In these dangerous times, we had reason to be worried about you. We hesitate to say it, but a few of us were anxious that you may have lost faith and left us.

All   We have seen the Lord!

Thomas   Unless I see the mark of the nails in his hands and put my finger in the mark of the nails and my hand in his side I will not believe.

Matthew   Thomas, we understand your doubts very well. And after all we ran away and …

John   No, Matthew, I did not run away. I stayed with those faithful women.

Matthew   Sorry, John. You are right. You did not desert him.

But, as I was about to say to you, Thomas, Mary Magdalen, Johanna and James' mother Mary, knew where Jesus was buried, having followed him to the end. We doubted all that Jesus had foretold about himself. We failed. And, Thomas, we are further ashamed to admit that it was a stranger, one of the Council, Joseph of Arimathea, who asked Pilate to release Jesus' body and who buried it in his own new tomb.

The women then went to embalm his body but they discovered that the tomb was empty. They said that two angels appeared to them. Again, we did not believe them even when they said that they were terrified. So, Thomas, we understand your disbelief. A stranger and some women were faithful, while we whom Jesus had chosen to lead his movement lost faith and ran away.

Bartholomew   Yes, Thomas, we understand. We did not believe either when Magdalen told us that she had met him in the garden, and that he told her to announce the good news of his resurrection to us, his brothers.

We rejoice that he still called us his brothers, and that his first words were to offer us peace in this very room. So we still keep our frail hearts open, as we await the Holy Spirit which he promised.

Resurrection Experiences

Johanna, Susanna and Magdalen talk about the Resurrection

Johanna
A strange journey together for all three of us. We surely needed the support of one another. I expected a good deal more response from the eleven but they certainly kept out of sight since Calvary. No! Let me think – they kept out of sight since Gethsemene. John showed a bit more courage than the others.

Susanna
Yes, a strange journey indeed. And now he has gone. How I miss him!

Johanna
No Susanna, he is not gone. He will always be with us, but in a different way; he is risen in each of us. It is a very deep presence, a lasting one and we must tell the world about it. For so many people God seems far away. They see him as an overseer or as a boss up in the sky. They spend their lives sincerely reverencing him and obeying him, often out of fear. Now we know that he is among us and in us.

Magdalen
How true, Johanna. His presence can never leave me. I learned so much when he asked me not to cling to him when we were in Joseph's garden. I am the tactile type as you know, and I loved him very much. Now I can cling to him in another way, forever in my heart; there will be no parting from him ever again.

Johanna
Of course, Jesus liked to hold people close too. I will never forget seeing how he touched Bartimeus's eyes, and I recall the admiration I felt for him when he walked out of the village holding the blind man's hand.

Susanna
And we will never forget how he embraced the children so gently and so lovingly.

Johanna
And he touched the lepers tenderly without reservation.

Magdalen
We were very blessed to be able to travel with him

and take care of his simple needs. Didn't young John have a big appetite? And the fishermen were always hungry too. Impulsive Peter ate very fast, didn't he?

Susanna   Having lived in the hills with his gang of Zealots really made Simon a bit greedy and did nothing to improve his manners, I thought.

Johanna   But he never asked me to return his knife when I borrowed it to clean the fish for the first time. Maybe the feminine presence civilized him a little.

Magdalen   Jesus talked a lot about poverty but he graciously accepted all the help that we gave him from our resources. Johanna, you were secure enough with your husband Chusa's good salary from Herod. Fortunately, Herod never discovered where some of his stewards' salaries ended up.

Susanna   But how did Jesus choose Judas to look after the money? Why did he not ask one of us to manage it? I found it very difficult each time I had to ask Judas for some money. He was always reluctant to part with it. Still, he must have been smart in his own way. Jesus did not seem to notice the money disappearing.

Johanna   What continues to amaze me about Jesus is a deeper and more obvious issue.

Susanna   What is that?

Johanna   Well, did you ever see a rabbi break the Law that forbids him to talk to or even be seen with a woman in public? No wonder they disliked him.

Susanna   And do you remember that masculine prayer – 'I thank thee, Lord, that thou has not made me a dog, a Samaritan or a woman'?

Magdalen   And what of the women who had devils inside them? He loved all of us despite all our faults and poured his love into us. I so loved him, and I know that he loved me. My heart warms every time I recognise that, after his resurrection, he chose me for his first appearance. Now he is risen and living in all of us.

Johanna   From the day we met him in Galilee, has it not been a great experience to travel with him, to be part of his community, and now to have him live in us and among us still?

Tell me, did any of us feel a bit uncomfortable when his apostles wanted to chase the mothers away? It is interesting to see how a little power goes to men's – sorry – people's heads. I thought that they might chase us away too, although the married apostles were clearly more at ease with us.

Susanna   When they were pushing the mothers away, Jesus was clearly very angry and he straightened them out promptly. I gave Peter a wide smile but he did not return it. The poor fellows! They were really embarrassed. I think they felt that they owned Jesus. I hope that their successors will not think the same ever again.

Magdalen   But deeper still. What a journey we had to Calvary on that Friday. I thought I would die myself as I witnessed the sheer savagery of the day.

It was only in supporting his beautiful mother that I was able to keep going. I thought that she would faint beside the cross but she managed to stand upright, supported by John and myself.

Johanna   Didn't Zebedee's wife redeem herself well when she stood there too, knowing in her heart that her two sons might suffer as Jesus did. Her ambition to have them sitting on two thrones must have finally melted at that moment.

Magdalen   Susanna, I felt sick, as I felt the pain of those blunt nails being hammered through my own hands. I so loved him.

Johanna   I seemed to lose all feeling in my feet as the hammer crashed down on the nails.

Susanna   John was there but where were the other eleven?

Johanna   Did you not hear what happened? Nine of them ran out of the garden and away. Peter denied knowing him and Judas sold him.

We were his only friends but of course, as women, we had to keep our distance. I think I can understand now why he appeared to us first.

Magdalen Johanna, do you remember the great sadness and the eerie silence as we travelled to bring the spices early the next day just before the Sabbath? We were wondering how we would get that big stone out of its hollow in front of the tomb! Once again, there were no men to be seen.

Johanna It was great that we managed to follow the funeral and that Joset's mother and yourself observed where they buried his body.

Magdalen Do you remember the shock at finding that the stone had been rolled back, and then to see an angel sitting on it? Emotional as I tend to be, I burst into tears and the angel said, 'Do not weep'. What an experience it was.

Johanna You recovered better than I did. I felt weak and I gasped with shock at what I was seeing. It was good that James' mother had a strong grip on my arm.

Magdalen Having looked into the tomb, do you remember how I bluntly stated the obvious: 'They have taken my Lord'?

Johanna And we will never forget the words of the angel: 'He is risen'.

Magdalen Despite all my hopes to see him alive again, I could not believe it had happened until I turned around in the garden and heard his voice. Even then I could not believe it; I thought he was the gardener. He must have wanted to ease my deep anxiety by asking the question, 'Who are you looking for?'

Johanna Yes, Mary, I remember it well. The message, 'He is risen', was almost too much for me also. I had some questions in my mind but I kept quiet.

Magdalen Then ... he said my name – Mary ...
And I clung to him until he spoke again, asking me to let go of him.

Johanna Was it then that he asked you to bring his message to the apostles?

Magdalen   Yes, but first he used my name, Mary, and then he said *Shalom*, and, as he so often had done before, he told us not to be afraid. I have never been afraid since. I love him so much, so much I could burst. No wonder we had the energy to run with the good news. I was the happiest messenger-girl in the world, on that day, at that time.

Johanna   Tell me again how the Apostles received you.

Magdalen   Their first response to the good news was to call it nonsense and to disbelieve everything. But, as you know, Peter and John heard me and believed enough of what I told them to run to the tomb to check if we women were really telling the truth. I had to smile when I heard that poor Peter was out of breath and unable to keep up with John. John always liked to be first on the scene.

Susanna   I feel bad that I missed out on so much during those last days but I am grateful that we are still together on the journey and that he is with us, and within us.

Magdalen   He is with us and within us always, yes, even to the end of time. Let us go back to the Temple and join with the apostles in praising God.

Johanna   Now we can look forward with joy to meeting him again on the Mount of Olives, as he has invited us to do.

Magdalen   Also to our meeting with Mary his mother, and with the apostles in the upstairs room for prayer. We are expecting the fulfilment of the promise of Jesus, that he will send what his Father has promised, so that his community will be clothed with power from on high.

Peter and John Remember

Peter and John Talk about
Their Call to Follow Jesus

John   My father Zebedee was very surprised when yourself and Andrew walked away from your boat and nets two years ago. Then, as you will remember, Jesus came further along the shore to where we were mending our nets. My father did not even look up at him, and he told us to keep at our work. Jesus then called us, as he did Andrew and yourself.

       I heard later that when our father told the story to our mother she thought she saw possibilities for us with this new preacher. She had strong ambitions and high hopes for both of us, and had often told us that fishing with broken nets was not very profitable.

Peter   I think your father could not have been more shocked than Andrew and I were when we came under the spell of Jesus, and especially when we felt liberated enough to leave our families and our livelihoods. For me it was as if The Holy One himself had called me; I felt compelled to go. My wife never recovered from the shock.

John   My brother James is more religious than I, and he reminded me that Abraham's call and faith-filled response is a model for all true Israelites. He left Ur of the Chaldeans, his country and his kindred, and he went off not knowing where he was going. Of course, I knew this well enough, but I felt I was no Abraham. I always liked to know where I was going.

Peter   Yes, Abraham's country, Mesopotamia, is a long way off in so many ways from our struggling business by the Lake of Galilee. Of course, Abraham was accepting an invitation with a promised reward of more land, a rich country, and fatherhood of a great nation. We simply got a very vague invitation to go fishing for people. It was only gradually that I began to understand the significance of all this. One of the last things Jesus said to me was that in my old age someone would lead me to a place where I would not choose to go.

John   It was the same day that you asked him about my future. Jesus told you to leave the decision regarding my future to him. I am gradually discovering that faith is much about not knowing, and about trusting him totally.

Peter   Looking over at that Bedouin's camel tied up across the street, reminds me of the day when he said that it was as difficult for rich people to get into heaven as it was for a camel to pass through the eye of a needle. I asked him how we, who had left everything to follow him, would be rewarded. Do you believe all that he promised?

John   Yes, I do. Jesus promised us that we would one day sit on 12 thrones judging the 12 tribes of Israel. I wished that my aspiring mother had heard that. It remains a promise, however, and promises always demand trust.

Peter   Trust, did you say? It is not so long ago, and after nearly three years with him and trusting him, that I said publicly I was going back fishing. My loss of faith spread very quickly. You all agreed to come with me. On that night we caught nothing. Then, just after daybreak, you recall that he appeared on the beach, and he asked us to throw out our net on the right side of the boat, and in an act of trust we obeyed him. We were rewarded with that big haul. My heart was still beating wildly as we sat on the shore that morning to enjoy the breakfast he had cooked for us.

John   Yes, no wonder you were so deeply affected. The man whom you called Messiah, the Son of the living God, was serving us. I was reminded of his words telling us that he had not come to be served, but to serve.

Peter   Are we called to serve The Holy One or is The Holy One serving us? Do you remember when he spoke to us at our last meal? He said that he loved us as the

Father loved him. That is surely serving us. Only then did he ask us to serve him in one another with the same love. On quite a few occasions, since hearing his request, I have lost my head and forgotten that I ever heard it.

John You absolutely lost your head on the day of the storm when you pulled on some clothes and jumped into the sea, after I said, 'It is the Lord'.

Peter No, I am thinking more of the denial and of my decision to return to fishing.

John You received a great boost a year ago, Peter – the day that we came back to the lakeshore and Jesus asked to use your boat, in order to pull out from the shore and speak to the crowd. I am sure that you wondered why he chose you, with your fragile boat and torn nets.

Peter I still cannot forget what went through my head when he asked us to row out further into the deep, and to put out our nets for a catch. My first thought was how presumptuous and naïve it was, for a carpenter from Nazareth to tell me how to run my business. So I told him that we had worked all night and we had caught nothing. However, I was beginning to trust him and so we obeyed him. My faith has a history of rising and falling.

John Then you had to call on us for help, when your nets began to tear with the huge catch. That result certainly built up whatever faith we had. In your excitement you told Jesus that you were not worthy even to be in his presence. Do you remember how all the fishermen laughed at your rare moment of humility, when you declared that you were a sinful man?

Peter Yes, that catch was an embarrassing moment for me. You too suffered serious embarrassment on the day when you wanted to call down fire and burn up the Samaritans. You certainly received a gentle rebuke, and you learned the distinction between destroying and saving.

John That was nothing compared with how James and I

felt when our ambitious mother elbowed her way through the crowd and asked Jesus to give us special seats in his kingdom.

He gave a very clear statement of the fact that suffering and worldly failure were inevitable for anyone who followed him. None of us foresaw that possibility at the time. As Abraham was looking for more land, some of mother's avarice existed in me. There was a lot of hope for personal status and success in the beginning as we began to feel superior to the priests, to the Scribes and to the Pharisees whom Jesus confronted so clearly.

Peter When Jesus brought your mother and yourselves down to earth, it was not unlike the moment when he called me Satan. He said that he – and presumably his followers – must suffer greatly and be put to death. Then I blurted out, 'Heaven preserve you. This must not happen to you'. I was thinking anxiously of where the possibility of his death would leave me.

Anyway, it is now becoming clear to both of us that Jesus' followers must be ready to suffer. How did we ever forget his words at our last meal, 'Servants are not greater than their master. If they persecuted me they will persecute you'?

John We must also admit to an even greater shock when he said that the Temple was coming to an end. That meant the end of many of our ideas about conventional religion and secular success. Big buildings do not seem to be part of his plan. He said that where two or three of us are gathered, he will be there with us.

We all took a step forward when you led us in confessing that he was the Christ, the Son of the living God. Yes, it was a great moment.

Peter But I am still shocked by his telling me to strengthen you all, and that he would build his chosen community, his *qahal*, on me, as on a rock.

I wonder did he know that the 'rock' he had chosen was so fragile. Did he realise how fragile I was when he said that Satan would sift me like wheat? At the same time, his assurance of his prayers for me gave me great strength for the future.

John   The details of your public denial are not known. When did it happen?

Peter   After his arrest when you got both of us into the governor's place. I stayed in the courtyard, and one of the maids recognised me and declared aloud that I was one of Jesus' followers. I not only denied him but I cursed and swore that I never knew the man. That was only a short time after I boasted that I would die with him. I even suggested that the rest of you might fail when the test came, but not I, not I. Imagine! He was so correct when he said that Satan would sift me like wheat.

John   Still, you spoke for all of us when he promised his flesh as food for his followers when many left his company. I recall your words, 'To whom can we go? You have the words of eternal life.' Over all, Peter, the two of us have been very privileged in spite of all our fumblings and failures.

Peter   Even as we ascended the mountain with him, I had questions and maybe some doubts about where it was all going to end. But what an experience awaited us there! You remember that I was overcome, totally overcome, and that I wanted to stay there. Was it not wonderful for us to be there with him?

John   And seeing Moses and Elijah, to know that both the Law and the Prophets were fulfilled in a carpenter from Nazareth who had chosen us, Galilean fishermen, to be so close to him.

Peter   Then there was the simple but soul-shaking revelation and directive which gives meaning to our lives, 'This is my beloved Son with whom I am well pleased. Listen to him'. Now hard-headed fishermen like me are not often fearful. However, at that time I was overcome by trepidation, until I felt his hand resting on my shoulder and I heard him say, 'Do not be afraid.'

John   Do you remember how, on the way down, we looked forward to telling the world about our experience?

That is, until he surprised us by telling us not to do so until he had risen from the dead. I asked James if that was what he had said, and James repeated the words, 'risen from the dead'.

Peter, it is no wonder I outran you to the tomb when I knew that I had heard his words correctly.

Peter I shared the thinking of all of you, that the women's story about his resurrection was nonsense. I was not ready to believe that Jesus would appear to women, to three of them, before coming to see us. It was beyond my power to believe he would do that. I mean we are his appointed leaders!

John What is your most unforgettable memory in all your time with him?

Peter Need you ask, John? You laughed with the others when It happened. It was in the boat when the storm blew up. Remember how he appeared to us in the semi-darkness. We were terrified. Most of us thought it was a ghost and we all gasped in fear until he said, 'Courage! It is I. Fear not'. As usual, I still doubted, and I yelled out a request that he call me out of the boat, but I added 'if it is you'. Then with a broad smile he called back, 'Come'. And I did. You know the rest. My transfiguration-faith failed me, and I could feel myself sinking. My most precious memory of Jesus came then, his hand reached out to me and he said, 'O you of little faith. Why did you doubt?' His strong hand. I will never forget it.

What is your abiding memory, John?

John My most unforgettable memory is the reaching out of his hand also. It was in the house of the synagogue president, when everyone was weeping and wailing over his daughter's death. Jesus said to him quietly, 'Do not be afraid; only have faith'. Then saying *talitha kum*, he reached out and took the little girl's hand in his ... his gentle hand. I will never forget that moment.

Judas and Barabbas

Judas and Barabbas Reflect on Their Failures

Barabbas Can you help me? I am a poor man and I am hungry, just out of prison. Your namesake, Judas the Galilean, was a friend of mine. At the riot during the census he was a great fighter, a great support to us, but he was killed. Was he a relative of yours?

Judas No, he was not, and I have no money to give you.

Barabbas But are you not the man who had charge of the purse for the Jesus group? The word is around that the priests gave you 30 pieces of silver to hand him over. You do not need all that. How about sharing a few shekels? I am in bad shape. And, anyway, Jesus and your group are gone. You are on your own; even the priests despise you.

Judas I feel more despised by myself; I detest myself. You have no idea what that feels like. I left the group and I have no money. I am in a hurry now. I need to talk to someone.

Barabbas Talk? About what?

Judas As you said, I was one of Jesus' group. He chose me right from the beginning when he started his movement. I was one of just twelve. I have lived with him for almost three years. And, yes, he trusted me with the common purse. I gradually saw that the net was closing in on him, and that he was getting nowhere with his talk of a kingdom. I felt it was time to get out and I did. There is no chance to return to him, even though in the garden, he called me friend as I pointed him out to the armed group sent by the priests and elders. The other apostles ran away, but I sold him.

Barabbas You are from Kerioth, are you not? Well, I knew one of the Jesus group, Simon the Zealot, before he joined you. He was on our side against the Roman savages. He would not join my riot, saying that it was not time yet. Then one day he told us that Jesus called him as he called you. He told us that he could not resist the invitation, because he had heard that Jesus might be the Messiah, the man who would set all of us free. Besides, he said that he was drawn immediately to this man, Jesus. Then he left us.

Judas   You are not listening to me. You see, I like Jesus too.

Barabbas   Well, he has gone now. He has been condemned to crucifixion.

Judas   Crucifixion?

Barabbas   Yes, crucifixion. 'Let him be crucified', the crowds roared. I was there; I heard it and I saw it all.

Governor Pontius Pilate gave the mob a choice, to save him or me, and urged on by the priests, the crowd chose to save. I will never forget the sound of the roar of the crowd, 'Give us Barabbas'. I could not believe what I was hearing, until Pilate ordered his guard to let me go. I am free now but I am hungry.

Judas   Tell me more about the end.

Barabbas   I know only that Pilate did try to save Jesus by talking to him at length, but in the end Jesus simply refused to talk with him. He had brought Jesus out on the lithostrotos and he told the crowd that he could not find any fault in him. That was the end of the conversation between Jesus and the governor. Pilate washed his hands in public and declared himself innocent of Jesus' death. They say that Pilate's wife had a dream telling her to ask her husband to have nothing to do with harming Jesus because he was a just man.

Judas   Have you told me everything?

Barabbas   Well, no. You would have felt sorry for Pilate. He was torn between the crowd's threats to report him to Caesar, the complexities of Jewish law, and his anxiety to set Jesus free.

Having heard that Jesus came from Galilee, Pilate

had him sent to his enemy Herod who was visiting Jerusalem at that time, hoping that it would solve his dilemma. It did not, but he and Herod became friends from that moment.

Pilate had Jesus scourged, and the soldiers crowned him with thorns. Then Pilate brought him out with a purple robe thrown around him, and he asked the crowd, 'Shall I crucify your king?' That incensed them and they yelled back, 'We have no king but Caesar'. That was brutal and dishonest, of course. They hate Caesar and everything Roman.

They kept playing on Pilate's weakness, until he finally brought me out, and asked them to make a choice between Jesus and me. They forgot that I led the riot in which many were murdered. I cannot understand it. It was a choice between a good man and me. You know the rest.

Judas   How true! He was a good man and now I know it is too late. I was a fool. Even as he washed my feet and I looked into his eyes, I had a feeling that I was evil, but that he was overlooking it. Just before that, he had folded a piece of bread, dipped it in the dish and handed it to me. It was such a clear offer of friendship, even then.

Barabbas   You made a very big decision in a hurry, but it is all over now.

Judas   No, it was not made in a hurry; it was a gradual but disastrous decision.

Much earlier, when Jesus promised his flesh to eat and his blood to drink, many people left him. I could hardly believe my ears when he asked all twelve of us if we wanted to leave him too. Impetuous Peter answered, 'Lord, to whom shall we go? We believe; we have come to know that you are The Holy One of God'.

We all agreed with Peter, but my heart was not in it, even then.

Barabbas   Why not?

Judas   Well, I was never very religious. My occasional visits to the Temple were motivated by human respect more than anything else – a conventional believer you might say. It was too much to ask me to believe that The Holy One of God was walking around the dusty roads, the cobbled streets, and that so often he was standing beside me wearing sandals.

Barabbas Temple-going was a rare experience in my life too. So I can understand your doubts. Besides, I believe the Temple is rotten, and the authorities are cooperating with the Romans when it suits them, but they are very powerful. Yes, Judas, you are a practical man; you knew that it was time to get out. You were right.

Jesus was on a collision course with a powerful system, from the beginning. I realize now that one has to keep one's head down and one's mouth closed in the presence of organized evil. To speak out or to revolt is dangerous. It does not matter who is suffering, so long as you survive.

Judas Most religious people accept this. They just pray for the oppressed, leave the evil system alone and ask The Holy One to change it. Jesus forgot this; he was too religious. That is why he was condemned and crucified. And most people, even religious people, are not willing to be crucified, even to help others.

But my problem and pain are different. Jesus must have seen me as a good, honest man when he trusted me to keep the purse. I wonder still why he did not notice that I was gradually helping myself out of the common fund. He trusted me totally. I do not understand much about this thing called love, but now I would say that he loved me.

Barabbas I have never experienced this thing called love, either as a child or among my companions on the street. We felt close during the riots, and when I saw the Temple guard striking one of my accomplices, I struck out and killed him. Was that love, Judas? I was going to be crucified for it.

Judas I do not agree with killing, but I was thinking about my own immediate welfare too. The system was closing in on Jesus because he continued to annoy the powerful religious leaders; I could see his end

approaching. He told me often to give some of our
money to the poor, and that really annoyed me.
Then, when he corrected me for commenting on the
woman who wasted expensive perfume on his feet, I
thought that I might as well help myself from time to
time.

Barabbas   Are you going to help me or not? I am starving.
Where is all the silver? Maybe you can assuage your
guilty feelings and make up to The Holy One – if you
still believe in him – by helping this hungry man.

Judas   I have no money. When I heard that he had been
arrested, I almost got sick. I knew I had made a
terrible mistake, betraying innocent blood. I returned
to the chief priests and the elders, asking them to
take the money back and release Jesus. They laughed
at me, and I immediately threw the silver – all 30
pieces – on the sanctuary floor.

In their religious scruples they called it blood
money that the Law forbade them to put into the
treasury. They refused to keep it, but used it instead
to purchase a cemetery for foreigners.

Barabbas   I do not believe that you foolishly parted with all
that money.

Judas   I know now that I was a follower of Jesus, maybe
a believer of some kind, but I was not a disciple.
I never let go of myself, even though I heard him
say so often that he wanted total commitment.
When the rich young Pharisee, who kept all the
commandments, was unable to let his money go, I
understood perfectly. Of course, we had little else in
common; he was a good man. And there are many
more of them.

Barabbas   You are very mixed up.

Judas   I am confused, guilty, lonely and yes, very mixed up.
Even in the garden, as I told you, he called me his
friend … and I kissed him … I am … I cannot find a
word to truly describe how I feel.

Barabbas   I am still hungry, Judas, I am starving. My stomach is
empty.

Judas   That is the word I need – empty! ... I feel empty, empty in a way that you will never understand, Barabbas.

Two Marys Meet

Mary Mother of Jesus consoles Mary Magdalen

Magdalen   Here we are, two women who have lived two very different lives and who came together at an extraordinary moment, at an extraordinary event, on the hill of Calvary.

Mary   That moment of our meeting – that terrible crucifixion of my son – can never be forgotten, by either of us.

Magdalen   Despite the dissimilarity of our life stories we were there side by side to see – no, to share in – the dreadful experience.

Mary   It was love that brought us together, Magdalen – great love for one man. Our loving was different, but both were great just the same.

Magdalen   How true it is, that our loving was different, and yes, how dissimilar our journeys have been.
Please tell me about the beginning of your journey. I am always eager to hear more about him. I can never know enough about the man who changed my life so radically.

Mary   Well, it began in my virgin womb when I responded in faith to an angel's delivery of God's invitation. For nine months I pondered, but still I could not understand. I knew that in some mysterious way God had looked on my lowliness and was doing great things for me. It was grace from the beginning to the end.

Magdalen   Before your marriage ceremony you must have lived in great fear of condemnation, of being isolated from your family, from the village people and even from your friends.

Mary   Yes, I lived in constant fear of rejection but Joseph was a just man who decided to put me away quietly until God told him about the origin of my child. You cannot imagine the relief it was for Joseph to receive the divine message, and for me to hear it from him.

The Bible stories about noble women, taught me by my father, have led me to trust God always. I think of the brave midwives, Shiprah and Puah, who disobeyed Pharaoh's order to kill male Hebrew babies. I think too of Pharaoh's daughter who rescued Moses, of our father Abraham's wife, Sarah, of Miriam who led the dancing liturgy at the Red Sea, of Hannah praying at Samuel's dedication, of Esther foiling Hammam's plan to exterminate our people. And of course I think of the Moabitess, Ruth, the great ancestor in the family of my husband Joseph.

Magdalen   Of course, your parents recited the *Shema* when you were born as was the custom in religious families. I can be reasonably sure that this was not so in my home. And we know too that boys were given their name at circumcision but a girl had to wait until her father was called, after her birth, to read from the *Torah* in the synagogue. My father was never called; he didn't even attend the synagogue.

Mary   Tell me more about your family and childhood.

Magdalen   Well, Mary, I never felt my parents loved me. I know that the birth of a daughter was rarely greeted with joy. Sirach even states bluntly, 'The birth of a daughter is a loss'. I grew up with a feeling of being unwanted, a burden and useless, even more than the average Jewish woman.

Mary   I hope you know that you are no longer unwanted. We all love you …

Magdalen   Yes, yes, and I know that Jesus loved me and that he still loves me. That is why I stayed with him to the end. And, of course too, my heart leaps with joy every time I remember that he called me by my name in the garden, because I know that rabbis were forbidden to speak to any woman in public.

Mary   Magdalen, it was right that he would speak with you, that he would recognise your deep commitment.

Magdalen   When I recall the experience of carrying around seven devils inside me, I shiver and I rejoice at the same time. The total acceptance of me by the other women who travelled with Jesus, gradually made me a new woman. The experience of returning with you from Jesus' burial by that noble councillor Joseph of Arimathaea in the early dawn, is unforgettable too. I thought we would never reach his home, just to sit with him and enjoy his great hospitality.

Mary   Also, you had the privilege of being the first public witness and missionary of God's good news. Just think, after his resurrection Jesus chose you to tell the community leaders the good news of his resurrection. I was the first to hear it and you were the first sent to spread it. Wonderful!

Magdalen   How I love him, even more than any woman loves her spouse. I know that he still lives in me.
    Now, tell me more about his early years.

Mary   Well, I had to live with the mystery of it all, especially when the angel told me that my child would be great and be called Son of the Most High, and that the Lord God would give him the throne of his ancestor David. It was all too much for me when the angel told me that the Holy Spirit would come upon me and that the power of the Most High would cover me with his shadow. My heart felt as if it was full of treasure which I could not begin to describe or even to understand.

Magdalen   But tell me about his childhood and growth.

Mary   The journey to Bethlehem and the birth in a stable were both severe trials. Looking down at my helpless baby tested my faith. The Son of the Most High was helpless at my breast.
    Then when we presented him in the Temple, Simeon's words about Jesus causing the rise and fall of many in Israel frightened me. When he told me that a sword would pierce my own soul too, I did not understand, but I added all these things to the treasure already within my heart.

Magdalen   Can I hear more about Jesus as he grew up?

Mary   As Simeon had foretold, he grew and became strong. He was filled with wisdom and he increased in divine and human favour. With the other children he enjoyed playing games in the street, playing flutes, pretending they were attending funerals and weddings. They made all sorts of toys from clay.

I relished the different names for the phases in his growing – *yonek* as he suckled at my breast; and *gamul* when he was weaned; then, when he was four years old he was a *taph* and he was helped to recite the Scriptures.

Joseph reminded me that special blessings were reserved for the man who rears his son in the *Torah*, and for the mother who sends her son to read the *Torah* parchment in the synagogue. It was beautiful to see him so happy going off each day with the other children on our street, to meet the rabbi.

At the same time Jesus began to learn his trade as a *tekton* from Joseph, and, like every other boy, at 13 he was known as 'a son of the Law'. It was moving to think of him beng now obliged to keep the 613 commandments and to wear phylacteries while at prayer. He was so excited when he put them on for the first time.

Needless to say, he was well liked by those who came to Joseph's workshop for their ploughs and pieces of furniture. It was interesting to see Joseph teaching him, and correcting his mistakes until he became proficient.

Magdalen   You must have enjoyed observing his growth to manhood.

Mary   Yes, indeed. At 18, as the oral laws say, he was fit for the bridal chamber; so we often had to listen to people whispering about him not being married, and they wondered why. Joseph and I wondered too. It was all part of the mystery which told me that the baby I had borne, the child whom I nurtured, and the young man I saw grow beside me, was mine, but somehow not mine. The Law said that at 20 a young man is free to pursue his own calling, and is bound to pay the Temple tax of half a shekel.

Gradually we were confirmed in our belief that he was different. We noticed that he spent long periods alone in prayer. Of course, since he was very young, he had seen me praying alone and he watched Joseph pause for prayer during his work.

Magdalen   How did you feel when he left home?

Mary   Joseph explained to me that the oral tradition tells us that at 30 a man is fit for authority and fit to discern and to teach.

Magdalen   Did you have any part in his religious education?

Mary   Yes, indeed I did. Joseph often quoted Deuteronomy to me, 'These words of mine, you shall teach them diligently to your children, and you shall talk of them when you sit in your house, when you walk by the way, when you lie down and when you rise'. I obeyed this willingly.

Jesus also told me that the rabbi taught him to recite these lines from Proverbs by heart: 'Hear, my son, your father's instructions and reject not your mother's teaching'.

Although as a girl I never studied the *Torah*, I knew that it was studied not just to learn proper conduct and action, but also as an act of worship. My only education was to study the complicated *arcana* of the dietary laws. I suppose you learned them too.

Magdalen   As I said, my parents were not religious. Going to the well was one of my duties but the upper class women rarely spoke to me in my ragged clothes. As you went to the well each morning, were you revered in Nazareth?

Mary   Not really. You recall the custom in Israel: before marriage, I was known as the daughter of Joachim, then I was called wife of Joseph. And now, as you know, I am called the mother of Jesus. Maybe I received more respect than you, but as you must know, adult women had no identity apart from their parents, husbands and children. It must have been even more difficult for you.

Magdalen   You and I not only had different upbringings, but we are very different now also. Surely, The Holy One loves you more than he loves me.

Mary   That is impossible for The Holy One, because he is love itself. He told us in Isaiah, that he has carved each one of us on the palms of his hands. He loves everyone of us equally and unconditionally.

Magdalen   Mary, as I embrace you, my very dear friend, pray that I will grow to believe this.

Glossary

Bar Mitzvah
This describes the Jewish celebration when a young man reached the age of 13 plus one day, giving him legal and religious responsibility and full membership of the congregation.

Corban
Anything given to God in fulfilment of a vow.

Diaspora
The dispersion of the Jews beyond Israel, or the Jews living outside Israel.

Ephah
An ancient Hebrew dry measure equivalent to the bath (about 40 litres or 9 gallons).

Essenes
There were about 4,000 members in the Essene sect, 200 of whom lived in Qumran, their most important centre. New members underwent a training like that for a religious order – a one-year postulancy and a three-year novitiate. They vowed to be reverent, just, to hate sinners, to obey superiors, to tell the truth, to share property and to keep their teachings secret. Their ritual baths and meals were of great importance. They lived ascetic lives withdrawn from the world around them.

Hallel Psalms
Psalms 113 to 118 were sung as part of the Passover ceremony. They were sung by Jesus and his apostles, at the last Supper, before they left for the Garden of Gethsemane. '*Hallel*' means praise.

Herod
This was the third Herod, called Herod the Tetrarch, who ruled successfully for 43 years. He had John the Baptist beheaded when John criticised his affair with Herodias. Pilate allowed him to try Jesus, but he just mocked Jesus and sent him back to Pilate.

Hin
A Hebrew unit of liquid capacity equal to approximately five litres (about one gallon).

Levites
A Levite was one of 24 groups in the lowest rank among the sacred ministers in the temple. Some assisted officiating priests, others were musicians and some were doorkeepers at the temple.

Mishnah – Oral tradition
An important collection of rabbinic laws, supplementary to the written Torah. In the time of Jesus, these existed as an oral tradition, and they were codified in the second and third centuries of the Christian era.

Pharisees
A group within Judaism, numbering about 6,000, who led strict lives in keeping with the Scriptures and who insisted on rigid separation from Gentiles. They stressed ritual purity and payment of religious dues. It was their concern for linking faithful adherence to the Torah with daily life that enabled Judaism to survive the destruction of the Temple in 70 A.D. Although the Gospels criticise them for allowing much of their zeal for the Law to degenerate into fanaticism and hypocrisy, many Pharisees were open to the message of Jesus – as, for instance, Nathanael and the rich young man whom Jesus loved.

Phylacteries
These were small boxes containing scripture verses, worn on the forehead and on the arm by devout Jews.

Priests
Priests were sacred ministers who offered sacrifices at the altar of holocausts and burned incense morning and evening at the golden altar. There were twenty-four classes, each of whom took turns for one week ministering in the temple. They wore a long linen tunic, an ornamented sash and a turban. They were supported by tithes and other offerings. Priesthood was hereditary, descending from the tribe of Levi.

Publicans
The occupying Romans farmed out the job of tax collecting to the highest bidder. Publicans, who took on this work, carried it out at cross roads and bridges. They were often guilty of merciless extortion and were hated by their own people who regarded them as traitors, plunderers and disloyal to their religion. Jesus condemned their injustice, but some of them, like Zacchaeus and Matthew, became his followers.

Rabbis
In Hebrew 'rabbi' is a respectful title meaning 'my lord', 'my master' or 'my teacher'.

Sadducees
These were of noble background and were associated with the Temple and with priestly families. Liberal in that they were willing to accommodate to Greek styles of life, they also embodied a conservative element in their insisting on a literal interpretation of the written Law. Thus they denied

the resurrection and the existence of angels – teachings that had emerged in oral tradition and which the Pharisees accepted.

Sanhedrin

The Sanhedrin was made up of 71 members which included the temple oligarchy and the leading men in the city who were mostly Sadducees and some notable Pharisees. They supervised the administration of the country and gave rulings on important religious questions. They appointed all lower court judges. Herod the Great took away their power but to ensure peace, the Romans enhanced their status. The Sanhedrin was presided over by the High Priest.

Scribes

These were the learned class and the authorities on the written law and on the oral traditions. After study and at the age of 30, a scribe had hands imposed on him while being given a tablet and a key. Many were noted for pride and hypocrisy but some of them such as Nicodemus, who visited Jesus privately, were sincere. Generally, they opposed the Sadducees. They were condemned by Jesus for burdensome additions to the divine law.

Shema

This is the central prayer of Jewish devotion: 'Hear, O Israel: the Lord our God is one Lord, and you shall love the Lord your God with all your heart, with all your soul and with all you strength, and the words which I command you this day shall be upon your heart, and you shall teach them diligently to your children, and shall talk of them when you sit in your house, and when you walk by the way, and when you lie down and when you rise' (Deuteronomy 6:4).

Synagogue

A place of assembly for local communities, used for worship, and also as schools, libraries and courts of law. The synagogue housed the sacred scrolls and the eight-branch candlestick burning before them. The ruler of the synagogue, the elders and the leading men had special seats facing the others. Jesus said that the Scribes coveted these seats.

Temple

At the centre of the Temple and behind a double curtain was the Holy of Holies which contained the stone on which rested the Ark of the Covenant. This Ark had once contained the two tablets of the law given to Moses. The Holy of Holies was entered only once a year by the High Priest. Outside that area was the Court of the Priests which the lay people could enter only to bring their sacrifices to the priests. Outside this area was the Court of the Laity, and beyond this was the Court of the Women. Beyond this again was the Court of the Gentiles where buying and selling went on.

Torah

The word means 'teaching'. It refers to the first five books of the Old Testament. These were believed to be God's word, that lives in the heart of every faithful Jew.

Zealots

Zealots were a revolutionary group working for the violent overthrow of Roman rule in Israel. Today, they would be called terrorists.

Zion

A hill in Jerusalem just south of the city walls. The term is used in the Hebrew Bible for the mount on which the temple was built or for the temple itself or symbolically for Jerusalem or even for Israel as a whole.

Zizits

The fringes or tassels on the corners of the Jewish prayer shawl (*tallit*).

Books Consulted

Albright, William Foxwell. *Archaeology and the Religion of Israel* (New introduction by Theodore J. Lewis; Old Testament Library; Louisville/London: Westminster John Knox Press, 2006). 247 pp. ISBN 0664227422

Alon, Azaria. *The Natural History of the Land of the Bible.* New York: Doubleday, 1978. 276 pp. ISBN 0385142226

Baron, Salo Wittmayer. *A Social and Religious History of the Jews.* New York: Columbia Press, 1993. 114 pp. IBSN 0231088566.

Bouquet, Alan Coates. *Everyday Life in the New Testament Times.* London: B.T. Batsford, 1970. 232 pp. IBSN 0713416718.

Freyne, *Seán. Jesus, a Jewish Galilean: A New Reading of the Jesus Story.* London: T & T Clark, 2004. 212 pp. ISBN 0567084671

Skrzynski, Henry. *The Jewess Mary Mother of Jesus.* NSW Australia: Chevalier Press, 1994. 457 pp. ISBN 086940136